HEALTHCARE CALL CENTER ESSENTIALS:

Optimize Your Medical Contact Center to

Improve Patient Outcomes and

Drive Organizational Success

PETER LYLE DEHAAN, PHD

Healthcare Call Center Essentials: Optimize Your Medical Contact Center to Improve Patient Outcomes and Drive Organizational Success
Copyright © 2022 by Peter Lyle DeHaan, PhD

ISBN
    978-1-948082-94-5 e-book
    978-1-948082-95-2 paperback
    978-1-948082-96-9 hardcover

Library of Congress Control Number: 2022905793

Published by Rock Rooster Books, Grand Rapids, Michigan

Credits:
    Developmental editor: Kathryn Wilmotte
    Copy editor/proofreader: Robyn Mulder
    Cover design: Taryn Nergaard
    Author photo: Jordan Leigh Photography

Patrons

The following companies generously helped cover the production costs of producing this book. Join me in thanking:

1Call

LVM Systems

MedCall Plus

To all my friends in healthcare call centers

Contents

Call Centers: The Future of Healthcare

Let Your Call Center Shine as an Essential, Distinguishing
Communication Hub of Your Organization

If you're part of a healthcare call center, you already know the essential role the call center plays in the provision of healthcare services. And you envision the even greater role it will play in the future. Now, with recent developments that accelerated the use of call centers to supplement or even replace in-person interaction, others—both within the industry and without—are beginning to realize it too.

Throughout my adult life, I've worked in and around the call center industry. In 2003 I launched *AnswerStat* magazine to serve as the "information hub for healthcare contact centers." One part of the publication is my "Vital Signs" column in each issue. For this book, I've taken the best of those columns, dusted them off, updated them, and compiled them in this resource.

Much of this information you'll already know, but my hope is that this book will also give you fresh ideas and valuable insights to move forward into a better tomorrow for your healthcare call center, the industry, and your career.

To accomplish this, I've divided the book into seven sections: management, staffing, operations, customer service, marketing and promotion, and technology and tools, along with seasonal considerations. I've grouped the chapters accordingly, though some items fit in multiple categories or even transcend categories.

Let's begin our exploration of optimizing healthcare call centers.

PART 1:

MANAGEMENT

Proper Call Center Management Is the Foundation of a Successful Operation

W e'll begin our discussion with healthcare call center management.

Many elements must come together for a call center to function as it should and provide both the expected and the desired outcomes. Yet without astute management to bring all these elements together and hold them in their proper place, everything quickly falls apart.

Though it takes a long time and much work for a wise manager to produce a successful call center environment, a well-functioning operation can quickly crumble under the direction of the wrong manager or through mismanagement.

Finding a Good Call Center Manager

Two Options to Locate Your Next Manager

"I need to find a good manager."

The statement is simple; one I've heard many times over the years. Despite the straightforward nature of this basic need, its successful realization is anything but easy.

Quite simply, if you make the wrong selection now, the future of your operation is in jeopardy. It only takes a few months of bad management to undo years of work spent building a smoothly functioning machine.

The problem is that the downward spiral goes unnoticed until it's too late to fix. By then, good employees have already left. Often these are the best agents, the ones who cared most about their job and who served patients with excellence. This demoralizes the remaining staff. They feel they're on a sinking ship. Some will stay out of loyalty, with the hope things will improve. Others remain due to inertia, lacking the motivation to look for a new job.

In the process, patients suffer and callers fume.

Despite the careful vetting process, employment screens, interviews, background checks, and personal references, your handpicked manager—the golden child you were sure would solve all problems—has failed to meet expectations. And, once again, the pressure of finding a good manager confronts you.

The options are deceptively simple. There are but two: promote from within or hire from the outside.

Promote from Within

When you promote existing call center employees into management positions, there are several items working in your favor.

First, you know them and their work ethic: they have a record of accomplishment, having proven themselves in other areas in your organization. Next, they have already demonstrated their skills and abilities. This may be as a shift supervisor, a trainer, a lead agent, or all three. Third, they know your operation and they won't require training in how your organization operates. Finally, they know the industry; they understand call center work and comprehend the challenges of being an agent.

The downside is that they seldom have management experience. This means they need management training, followed by close supervision as they grow into their job. This won't happen quickly. If you move too fast, turning them loose before they are ready, expect disaster to occur.

Along the way, they will make mistakes. You hope the mistakes will be minor and their successes will outweigh their errors. But, of course, you can never know this in advance.

Hire from the Outside

The alternate approach is to hire an experienced manager. This solves all the issues surrounding management training. Yes, the new manager will still require some oversight in the beginning, but the timeframe shouldn't be as lengthy as for someone with no managerial experience.

The new manager will also need training specific to your organization and call center operation. They may even need to learn about the healthcare industry, but these areas are much easier to teach than general management skills.

The disadvantage of hiring from the outside is that you have no history together. You don't know their work ethic, their drive, or their ability to lead your call center or function in your organization.

Hiring a manager from outside your organization who has call center experience in healthcare is a rare combination that's hard to find. You can aim for this outcome, but be prepared to accept some concessions when making your selection.

Summary

Having the right manager is key to a successful operation.

There's no easy answer when hiring a call center manager. Finding the ideal candidate is a challenge, but that's what makes operating a call center interesting.

Is Your Call Center a Profit Center or a Cost Center?

Positioning Yourself as a Profit Center Will Help Drive Budget Success

When consulting for a hospital call center, I learned that the organization's marketing manager identified their call center as their most cost-effective form of marketing, offering the highest return on investment (ROI). It was a profit center.

Further surprising was learning that the entire call center operation fell under the budget of the marketing department. I suspect the call center director had little trouble getting the appropriate budget each year to operate the call center.

The opposite of a profit center is a cost center.

The Benefits of Being a Profit Center

If your call center generates revenue—either directly or indirectly—you stand a much better chance of coming out on the plus side for each year's new budget. If you're a pharmaceutical or durable medical equipment manufacturer, it's easy to make your case. You track sales, which you then use to offset the cost of your operation. Any expense that produces more sales becomes an easy request to justify.

Even if your call center doesn't directly handle sales or take phone orders, you can still work to establish yourself as a profit center. It just takes a bit more effort. For example, if you're a hospital call center, look for ways that you contribute to the revenue stream of your organization.

The Downside of Being a Cost Center

If upper management views your operation as a cost center, they'll see your line item on their budget as an expense to control and decrease whenever possible. This results in a scarcity of funds and makes it hard to operate a call center as needed to produce the best outcomes for patients and callers.

Each new budget cycle produces a predictable challenge of fighting to maintain the status quo of your funds. And receiving approval for additional expenditures on software, services, and initiatives to better serve your organization's patients looms as a formidable challenge.

If this is your reality, I feel for you. But there is hope: reposition your call center as a profit center.

How to Become a Profit Center

Each time you make a referral to a physician or clinic in your system, what's the value of that connection? Even more significantly, what is the lifetime value of that new patient to your organization? Suddenly that single phone call has a value of thousands or tens of thousands of dollars, or even more.

What about appointments? Each time you set an appointment for one of the providers in your system, what is its revenue potential, especially if that initial interaction leads to a series of follow-ups? Though these subsequent appointments may or may not go through your call center, the additional engagements would not have occurred had you not secured the first one.

Without your call center, these things wouldn't have happened. As such, you deserve credit for the critical role your call center played in bringing this new business—and revenue—into your organization.

Start tracking these types of revenue-producing transactions. But don't just note the number of calls. Instead, report the immediate value and long-term revenue potential from each of these interactions. In doing so you'll help shift your call center operation from a cost center to a profit center. And this will make a significant difference when it comes time to negotiate next year's budget.

Mixing Full-Time and Part-Time Call Center Staff

Discover the Right Balance in Agent Scheduling for Your Healthcare Contact Center

Some healthcare call centers only employ full-time staff. Others do the opposite and only hire part-timers. In most cases, the ideal solution balances a combination of full-time and part-time agents.

Full-Time Call Center Agents

A key benefit of staffing your call center with full-time employees is greater stability and predictability. A full-time employee with benefits, especially healthcare coverage, is more likely to be committed to their work and less likely to seek a new job.

This commitment results in having an accomplished workforce that possesses the knowledge accumulated only through longevity. The typical result is more accurate communication with callers and the potential for better outcomes. With these as the benefits of having a full-time staff, why wouldn't every call center want to hire only full-timers?

Call centers with only full-time staff face a couple of limitations. One is that call traffic doesn't fit the nice nine-to-five work schedule of full-time employees. Instead, callers arrive in predictable surges throughout the day. When attempting to address these traffic peaks with full-time staff working eight-hour shifts, the result is they will need to work like crazy some of the time and still not be able to keep up. At other times they won't have enough to do.

Another limitation is a lack of flexibility. If a full-timer's shift is over after eight hours, but you need them to stay late to take more calls, then you're looking at an overtime situation. On the other hand, if employees are sitting around twiddling their thumbs, you can't send a full-time employee home early because then they won't get the forty hours of work that you promised and the paycheck they expect.

Part-Time Call Center Agents

Because of these limitations, other call centers hire only part-time staff. This gives them maximum scheduling flexibility: they're able to have employees work exactly when they need them to, no more and no less. If things get especially busy and you need someone to stay later, many are happy to pick up extra hours. Conversely, if it's slower than expected and you want to send staff home, there's usually someone anxious to accommodate.

Yet this maximum flexibility comes at a price. Part-time staff are less committed to you, your call center, and your patients. They're more likely to look for other jobs that pay more, have better benefits, or offer more appealing schedules. They may desire full-time work and only accepted your offer because the hours you offered them were better than no hours at all.

This means that a call center of part-time employees has higher turnover, and all the problems that the constant churn of employees can present.

Hybrid Staffing

The solution is to strategically hire a mix of full-time *and* part-time employees. This provides the best solution to achieve both a degree of stability and much-needed flexibility. Though the ideal ratio of full-time to part-time workers varies from one call center to the next, a general initial goal is fifty-fifty. This provides a foundation of full-time employees filling half your typical schedule, with part-time staffers filling the rest.

In your actual operation, however, you may find it works better to have fewer full-time agents or to have more. Initially, however, you won't know what the ideal ratio is and will have to home in on it over time.

Call center staffing is part art and part science, balancing your organization's fiscal responsibility with your caller's healthcare needs. A hybrid staff comprised of both full-time and part-time agents may be the best way to get there.

Successfully Working from Home

Discover How to Effectively Work in a Home Office

I recently celebrated twenty years of working from home. During the first year I split my time between my home office and a traditional office. Then for a few years I divided my time between travel and working from home. But for the last sixteen years I've worked exclusively from home. It's an ideal arrangement, and I wouldn't have it any other way. In fact, I doubt I could ever return to a job that required me to go into an office to work each day.

But not everyone is like me. I chose to work from home. For others, circumstances forced them to vacate their call center workstation and set one up in their house. For some, this work-from-home scenario was temporary, while for others it has become their status quo.

Regardless of the situation or degree of permanence, here are some key considerations to make a work-at-home scenario a success.

Workspace

A key element to effectively work from home is to have a dedicated workspace you can call your own. For me, an unused bedroom became my office. When I'm in my home office, I work. When I leave, I stop.

But not everyone has a spare room they can take over. If that's the case, can you carve out a corner in another room? Can you make a room multifunctional, serving as an office during working hours and family space the rest of the time? The goal is to train yourself so that when you do go to your office—whatever it may look like—you're conditioned to work and not do anything else.

Distraction Free

Having a workspace without distractions is ideal, but it's not always feasible. In that case, the goal is to reduce distractions as much as possible. Remove everything from your home office that you don't need for work. This includes your phone, television, radio, and books. Delete games from your computer, as well as other programs that don't facilitate work.

Some home workers buy a white noise machine, turn on a fan, or listen to instrumental music so they can tune out household activities that may occur as they're trying to work. If you have an office door, close it. Post office hours in your work area. Then enforce them.

Expectations

Establish expectations with family and friends. When I began working at home, I told our young children that until 5 p.m. they were not to interrupt me for any reason unless they were sick or bleeding. That did the trick. Other family members were a bit harder to train, but the point is to insist that your family and friends respect your time in your home office as sacred and not assume you're available for nonwork activities. This also means not answering your home phone or taking personal calls while working.

Routine

Just as you have a series of steps you do before work and after work in an office location, do the same for your home office. Though it's quite feasible to do so, don't work in your pajamas. It conditions you to not take work seriously or put forth your best effort.

Don't eat meals or snacks in your office. Eat breakfast before you arrive, enjoy supper afterward, and leave your office for lunch. Doing so promotes focus, priority, and professionalism.

Tools

An effective office requires tools. First up is a fast and stable internet connection. I can't think of a job you can do from home for long without internet access. Get the best that you can afford, and don't let online access hinder your success when you work from home.

A slow or buggy computer is another detriment. Every second of delay or frustration at your computer is time you're not being productive. These seconds add up to minutes and minutes add up to hours. Again, get the best computer you can afford. Install all the same programs on your home computer as you have at the office. Don't skimp.

Look for tools that you may not use in your workplace office, such as Skype or Zoom, so you can connect with coworkers and your boss or subordinates as needed.

Schedule

If your work-at-home situation is direct contact center work, then your scheduler will tell you when to work.

For everyone else, establish your own schedule, just as you would in a workplace setting. Start at a specific time, end at a specific time, and take time out for lunch and breaks. The rest of the time you should be in your office working.

However, outside of your work schedule you should not be in your office working. This takes us to the final consideration.

Balance

We often talk about work-life balance. Though always a critical consideration, balance looms as an even bigger challenge when you work and live in the same place. This means segregating your work from the rest of your life, even though both happen at the same location. Some people prefer the word *compartmentalize*: to place work in one mental compartment and your home life in another.

Action Steps

If you find yourself working at home, put these tips into practice as soon as possible. Then you will be more likely to experience a successful, enjoyable, and effective situation.

If you're planning to one day work at home, put these steps into place before you start. It will make all the difference.

When done right, working at home can increase productivity, decrease stress, and improve your enjoyment of your work. Though you might now be working at home as a temporary solution to a problem outside your control, you might find the results so beneficial that you want to turn working at home into a permanent scenario.

Send Your Call Center Back to School

Now Is an Ideal Time to Enhance the Skill Level of
Your Telephone Staff

Too often the healthcare call center industry spends so much time focusing on the crisis of today that it squashes all thought about planning for tomorrow. Once you slip into crisis mode out of necessity, it becomes easy to stay there out of habit—even if there's no longer any reason for it.

We may stand at that juncture now.

This means it's time to balance your work for today with taking initiative to prepare for the future. If you don't, you won't make forward progress; you'll merely survive. Survival is necessary, but you need more if you ever hope to find success and enjoy fulfillment for yourself, your staff, and your organization.

One aspect of future preparation is education. This can be formal or informal, structured or ad hoc, mandated or self-determined. Though the application relates to everyone in the call center from new hire to director, let's—by way of example—consider this for your telephone agents. I'll leave it to you to extend this throughout all staff in your operation.

Refresher Training

When you think of your call center staff going back to school, consider refresher training for the first initiative. It never hurts to revisit the basics. Though it may feel as though your existing staff has moved beyond this elementary teaching, the basics can atrophy over time.

Agents forget instructions. Or maybe they never fully grasped some rudimentary skill to begin with, even though they seem to be doing well in their jobs overall. The problem is that determining which teaching to refresh varies from one person to another. Therefore, it's good to review everything.

Yes, I already hear your staff complaining. But this refresher initiative doesn't—and shouldn't—take as long as the first time. It should go much faster. Perhaps you can condense a day's worth of training into an hour—or even less. But the important thing is to make sure these basic skills don't slip away over time.

Application Instruction

A second option for going back to school is to look at application tutoring. When new software or an app enters your call center, agents need to receive training to know how to use it. Too often the urgency of the moment cuts this training short; sometimes it's even omitted. This forces your phone agents to figure it out on the fly. Though this may seem pragmatic or feel necessary, on-the-job training frustrates employees who want to provide excellent service, and it's disrespectful to callers who expect to receive it.

Therefore, provide complete training on all new software applications and major updates. Everyone will appreciate receiving this much-needed instruction.

Skill Enhancement

After reviewing the basics and mastering call center software apps, next go back to school to enhance skills.

Your telephone staff receives initial onboarding training when they're hired. As they go about their daily work, they apply that training and slowly build upon it to increase their skill level. But this isn't enough to ensure excellence, let alone produce successful outcomes. Your seasoned staff is ready for more. They need more. And you can provide it for them by teaching them advanced call center service techniques.

This may relate to customer service skills, problem resolution techniques, or de-escalating angry callers. It could also cover the seldom-used but much-appreciated advanced options available on using the vast power of your software platforms and databases to their full potential. Staff won't use these skills often, but when the situation arises, possessing the knowledge of these advanced techniques can make the difference between an unsuccessful interaction and a positive outcome.

Conclusion

Each fall, students return to the classroom. Do the same thing for your call center staff. Providing refresher training, application instruction, and skill enhancement will help them do their jobs with greater efficiency and produce higher-quality outcomes.

Don't let another year go by without giving your staff this much-needed support. The result will be happier employees and better-served patients—in addition to a more effective call center operation.

Tap Outsource Call Centers to Lighten the Load

Consider Outsourcing to Better Manage Call Traffic and
Increase Patient Access

As your healthcare call center grapples to deal with more calls than ever before, you seek ways to maintain the service level you provide to callers. Common ideas include using automation, increasing employee schedules, and hiring more staff.

A fourth option is to outsource calls to another call center that specializes in taking calls for other healthcare organizations. Many call center managers recoil at the thought of outsourcing. e=``TheThen They fear a loss of control, decrease in quality, or drop in status within the organization.

But before you dismiss this as a bad idea, consider four common types of outsourcing scenarios.

Outsource Certain Call Types

Analyze the types of calls you answer and the appropriateness of your existing staff to take them. As an example, assume you handle triage calls, appointment schedules, and call transfers, as well as provide medical answering service. Note the number of calls and the amount of time you spend in each category. Now document how many agents can take each of these call types and the number of hours they work each week. See how well your staffing aligns with your call types.

Next identify the biggest gaps. By way of example, let's assume you discover triage nurses taking routine messages for doctors. This is a huge mismatch. What if you send routine calls to your outsourcing partner, thereby freeing your nurses to do what they do best?

Of course, the opposite scenario might be too many triage calls and not enough nurses. You can outsource those, too, but it might be to a different outsourcing partner, one that specializes in telephone nurse triage.

Outsource Overflow

Another scenario that's ideal for outsourcing is the unexpected times when call traffic exceeds the schedule you've carefully devised to meet the projected call volume. Instead of having calls pile up in queue, reroute them to your outsourcing call center partner.

Outsource Specific Times

Third, look for daily or weekly patterns to see how well staffing matches up with traffic. You may discover—or confirm—that your third shift staff doesn't have enough work to keep them comfortably busy. Outsource those third shift calls to your outsource partner. Then move your third shift employees to second.

Of course, depending on the type of work your operation handles, you could have the opposite scenario, where not much happens during regular business hours and most of the action happens on evenings and weekends. So outsource first shift weekdays and reallocate those personnel to evenings.

Outsource Specific Days

Let's assume you have difficulty scheduling enough agents to handle your Sunday traffic. You can save yourself the hassle by sending those calls to your outsourcing call center partner and shutting down your call center on Sundays. Then you can reschedule your few Sunday employees to other days of the week.

Conclusion

Many call center managers summarily dismiss outsourcing. Yet today's leading healthcare call center outsourcers provide a high quality of service, often matching or even exceeding their client companies. Just vet them with care and make your decision based on outcomes, not price.

When you consider the benefits of being able to reallocate your staff to where they're most needed and to better serve your patients and callers, outsourcing is a viable option that warrants careful consideration.

Be Careful What You Measure

What Gets Measured Gets Done, and What Gets Paid for
Gets Done Better

C all centers measure many things. Some metrics are helpful, while others are misleading. Choose the ones you focus on with care. Tie incentives to those that matter most and aren't subject to agent manipulation.

My first full-time job was repairing copy machines. I didn't necessarily like the work, but I liked *having* work. Not only did I grab the first offer that came my way, but I also failed to verify the compensation, assuming what my school's placement department told me was correct. It was not. The company only paid about half of what I expected, so I considered this position temporary right from the onset—something to pay the bills until I could find work that paid better.

Nevertheless, I poured myself into my new job, striving to excel at fixing copy machines. I applied myself and became good. Quite good, in fact. I repaired the machines fast, kept expenses down, and earned praise from my customers.

Imagine my dismay when I saw my first technician ranking. I was near the bottom of the list. Something was wrong.

The dispatcher calculated the results for my boss, so I asked her what she tracked. I listened carefully. To my surprise, the measurements had nothing to do with repairing machines quickly or saving money. Most metrics addressed other factors such as the ratio of drive time to service time, the number of hours logged, and how many leads I passed to the sales department.

From this perspective, I was doing everything wrong.

Taking this knowledge, I developed a fresh approach to my job. I stopped focusing on serving customers. I began striving to maximize my rating because my numeric results determined my incentive pay. I desperately needed to earn a nice bonus to offset my lower-than-expected salary.

When the next ranking came out, I was near the top for the month, and my year-to-date placement had moved to the middle of the list. However, my paycheck was my real reward. For the third month, I was number one, and year-to-date I was in the top quarter. After six months, both my monthly and annual rankings were number one. My bonuses now approached my base pay. By playing their game, I'd nearly doubled my compensation.

Though I was still a good copy machine technician, the customer was not number one; my paycheck was. I didn't prioritize repairs based on urgency. Instead, I scheduled them to minimize my drive time, since part of the bonus was for spending less than 10 percent of my time behind the wheel. I'd start and end the day with a stop close to home because driving to my first call and returning home didn't count in the calculations. I also drove faster, but that's another story.

I no longer tried to save the company money but instead focused on what was best for my rating. For example, if protocol called for cleaning a filter or retrofitting a part, I'd replace it. Though this cost the company more, it eliminated the possibility of me receiving a call back for the same problem—and getting penalized as a result. If one of two parts would fix the problem but only time would tell which one, instead of replacing the cheaper part first and then waiting, I'd replace both to make sure.

No one realized what I was doing. My rating was stellar, my superiors were pleased, and customers couldn't tell the difference.

After nine months, a better job came along. The base pay for my new position exceeded the salary and bonuses of my old one. There were no games to play with my new employer. All I had to do was focus on the work.

Consider my story of repairing copy machines as you determine what you'll track and reward for your call center agents. Continue reading for more ideas of what to measure.

Beware the Time Bandits

Treat Your Call Center Labor like Inventory and Track It with Care

In retail, the term *shrinkage* euphemistically refers to stock which *disappears* before it can be sold. It is a product that the retailer bought but can't sell because someone stole it. To be direct, shrinkage is theft. While some of this is due to shoplifting, it also results from employees.

Regardless of the source or motives, shrinkage hurts everyone in the form of higher consumer prices and lower company profits. This affects jobs and threatens the business's future viability. Some retail operations take a surprisingly relaxed position about shrinkage, viewing it as an inevitable cost of doing business, whereas others see it as theft and take aggressive steps to eliminate or at least reduce it.

Shrinkage in the retail environment has an analogous application to the call center. True, a call center does not have tangible inventory that can disappear. Rather, a call center's inventory is human capital, that is, the call center schedule. Shrinkage in a call center, therefore, is agents who are *on the clock* but aren't processing calls. We see this manifested by agents who are not at their stations when they should be, are not logged in, are not *in rotation*, or are using some trick to block calls.

Like retail, some call centers take a surprisingly relaxed position about this shrinkage of their schedule, also viewing it as an inevitable cost of doing business. Their response is intentional overstaffing. But this only serves to cover the problem, not resolve the underlying cause.

Other call centers see shrinkage as little more than stealing— stealing time. Like their retail counterparts, they take aggressive steps to eliminate or at least reduce it. Call center shrinkage hurts everyone, resulting in a lower service level offered to patients, increased call center labor costs, decreased morale, and potentially less compensation for agents.

There are three factors that help track, explain, and counter call center shrinkage. They are adherence, availability, and occupancy.

Adherence

Adherence is a measurement of the time agents are scheduled to work compared to the time they actually do. Why is adherence important? Quite simply, it's because the ideal agent schedule aligns with projected traffic. When staff don't work their full schedule, the result is understaffing. In an ideal situation, staff should adhere 100 percent to their schedules. Unfortunately, this is often not the case.

To best track adherence, compare logged in time to scheduled time. Most call center managers are shocked the first time they look at this data, which can show huge unnecessary costs to the call center, as well as contribute to lower service levels.

Several factors can account for differences between the time scheduled and the time worked.

The first area comes from scheduled breaks, lunches, and training. This is the only acceptable contributor to adherence discrepancy. Depending on the length of breaks, the best resulting adherence will be around 90 percent. Forty-five minutes of breaks in an eight-hour shift will result in an adherence of 90.6 percent (7.25 hours out of 8).

The second consideration is absences, late arrivals, and early departures. Without filling these openings, the result is a disparity between the schedule and the fulfillment of that schedule. If this missed work results in paid time off, such as paid sick time, then there is both a dollar cost and service impact that results.

The third area is unscheduled breaks or any other distraction that causes agents to leave their positions. When factoring all these items together, it is common for call centers to have adherence rates around 75 percent, although well-run centers could be in the low 90s (as determined by their established break schedule).

Availability

A second staffing metric is availability, a subset of adherence. Of the time staff is adhering to their schedule, availability measures how much of that time they are ready (that is, available) to answer calls.

Calculate this by comparing available time (also called *on time*, *in rotation*, or *ready*) to logged in time. Specifically, it is the resulting percentage from dividing available time by logged in time. Although the ideal goal of 100 percent availability is achievable (that is, ready to process calls all the time they're logged in), 98 percent to 99 percent is more realistic.

Agent availability is strictly within the control of agents. It's determined by each agent's willingness to keep their station in a state of readiness to receive calls. Simply put, it is being available to answer calls.

Occupancy

Occupancy is the amount of time agents spend talking to callers compared to the time they are available to do so. To calculate occupancy, divide the total agent time (that is, talk time plus wrap-up time) by agent "on" time. This should be determined for each agent as well as for the entire call center.

Although it's possible to have 100 percent occupancy, the corresponding service level would be poor and unacceptable. One hundred percent occupancy means that agents are talking to callers the entire time they're logged in. It also means there are calls continuously in queue, waiting for the next available agent.

The resulting call center efficiency is great, but callers can end up waiting in a queue for several minutes or even over an hour. Therefore, 100 percent occupancy does not produce quality service and can lead to agent burnout and fatigue.

Interestingly, ideal occupancy rates vary with the size of the call center. Smaller centers can only achieve a low occupancy rate (perhaps around 25 percent) while maintaining an acceptable service level. Conversely, large call centers can realize a much higher occupancy rate (90 percent and higher) and still maintain that same service level.

This dynamic relationship between occupancy rates and call center size is the underlying impetus for call center consolidation. It's a profound example of economies of scale. Call centers in the range of ten to twenty seats typically see occupancy rates around 50 percent.

Conclusion

Call centers with poor adherence, availability, and occupancy rates can spend twice as much labor to produce the same service level as a comparably sized well-run call center. Calculate your center's adherence, availability, and occupancy numbers—and then take steps to improve them.

Don't let agent shrinkage lead to expense explosion.

Real World Staffing Examples

*Two Case Studies to Demonstrate the Critical Impact of
Adherence, Availability, and Occupancy*

Let's consider these metrics of adherence, availability, and occupancy as they relate to two medical call centers, specifically medical answering services. The first is a well-run operation; the second, a mismanaged one. They're about the same size, and both have a realized occupancy rate near 50 percent.

Call center A has an adherence rate of 90 percent and an availability rate of 95 percent, along with the aforementioned 50 percent occupancy rate. This means that for each 8-hour shift there are 3.42 hours of on-line time or actual work (8 hours x 90 percent x 95 percent x 50 percent).

Call center B has an adherence rate of 75 percent and an availability rate of 65 percent (with the same occupancy rate of 50 percent). For each 8-hour shift there are only 1.8 hours of on-line time or actual work (8 hours x 75 percent x 60 percent x 50 percent).

Although the result for call center A, a well-run operation, may be surprising considering how low it is, the corresponding number for call center B is shocking. In fact, to maintain the same service level, call center B would need to schedule 1.9 times as many hours as call center A. Consider what a significant impact this would have on labor costs and departmental expenses.

Lest you think that these are unrealistic numbers, both are real situations from call centers I've visited. It takes a concerted and ongoing management effort to be like call center A, while all too many operations are more like call center B. I challenge you to run your numbers to see how you compare—and then take steps to improve them.

Don't let these time bandits steal from you anymore.

Call Center Metrics

Beware Pursuing Arbitrary Statistical Results that Don't
Align with your Call Center's Size, Function, and Workload

P eople often contact me in search of information about medical call centers. Whenever possible, I direct them to content on the 1,200-page *AnswerStat* website. These queries are the easy ones.

However, often the inquirer asks about benchmarking and statistical issues for medical call centers. This is frequently initiated after the boss comes back from a convention or hears about the impressive statistical achievements from another call center. Often the message is simply, "Match these numbers."

Common targets are often arbitrary occupancy rates or labor percentages, but since each operation is different, it's unwise to blindly assume that the results at one operation are achievable at another.

Consider the following:

Occupancy Rate

A frequent area of interest is figuring out an acceptable agent occupancy rate. (Agent occupancy is the percentage of time that an available agent is processing calls or information.) There is a trade-off between occupancy rates and various customer service-related metrics, making the optimum occupancy point hard to determine. Although it may seem insolent, the correct answer to this question is, "It all depends."

First, it depends on the form and function of the call center. Centers that handle multiple contact points, such as phone calls and email, will realize a higher occupancy rate, since non-time-critical activities (processing email) can occur at slow times or between time-critical activities (answering calls). Also, some centers fill agent idle time with ancillary support activities, such as data entry, transcription, callbacks, and so forth. Again, this allows occupancy rates to increase.

However, the size of the call center is the main variable, affecting both feasible and ideal occupancy rates. I've heard of call center occupancy rates as low as the mid-twenties and as high as the mid-nineties, and everywhere in between. In specific circumstances, any of these results could be the appropriate occupancy rate. Conversely, they could also be the wrong ones. The key reason for this hinges on the primary reason for call centers in the first place, economies of scale.

The smallest staffed call center will have one person working per shift, 24/7. There will be times when this solitary agent is extremely busy (peak daytime traffic) and other times when few calls come in (the middle of the night). As such, occupancy rates will vary throughout the week, from quite low to moderately high.

There is also a tendency for calls to bunch up. In my publishing company most of my interaction with readers, authors, and vendors happens via email; the phone seldom rings. I can go several hours without a phone call, only to have two arrive at once. I talk to the first caller, while the second goes to voicemail. In a one-person call center, this second call would go into the queue and wait for the "next available agent." With only one agent, the wait could be substantial. Even though the occupancy rate will still be low, the service level has eroded.

You can increase the occupancy rate of a one-person call center by driving more calls to it—perhaps via marketing or assuming additional work—without increasing staffing. As such, there will increasingly be callers in queue, hold times will mushroom, and the average answer time will skyrocket. The only way for a solitary agent to realize a high occupancy rate is to have calls continuously in queue.

Although the answer to the occupancy question depends on many factors, small call centers can generally only achieve average occupancy rates in the mid-twenties to upper thirties. Attempting to push rates higher will result in call center suicide: long hold times, high abandonment rates, disgruntled and complaining callers, and stressed-out agents.

As call centers get larger, efficiencies increase, and there are more agents available to handle the calls in queue more quickly. Traffic spikes become easier to deal with, as there are more agents available to answer calls. The midsize call center can experience occupancy rates hovering around 50 percent.

Larger call centers enjoy even greater economies of scale and can better respond to traffic peaks, keeping agents occupied a higher percentage of time while still maintaining an acceptable service level. Occupancy rates in the seventies become a realistic goal.

However, it is the exceptionally large call centers, with hundreds of agents, that can experience call center nirvana, providing acceptable service levels even as their agents chug along at occupancy rates in the nineties.

So what's the ideal occupancy rate? It truly all depends. I'm not being cavalier, merely honest.

Labor Percentage

Another common item of interest is determining the appropriate percentage of expenses spent on labor. Here, too, "it all depends," with call center size again being the primary variable. Within the smallest of call centers, there is a potential for overhead to be low—which is a good thing—and therefore labor costs will be high.

This is even more pronounced if the manager is involved in taking calls. Managers can handle administrative and support tasks between calls and at slow times. As a result, all functions in the small call center can be highly integrated and efficient; this means low overhead. As a result, the percent of expenses spent on labor could therefore be upwards of 70 percent or more.

When call centers increase in size, a disproportionate amount of effort and expense go to a quickly expanding corporate, management, and control structure. Then they need shift supervisors, customer service staff, a scheduler, and so on. As a result, a much higher percentage of expenses become allocated to non-agent areas, with the percentage spent on agent labor correspondingly decreasing. Midsize call centers can be the most inefficient overall, with agent labor percentages dropping below 50 percent.

For larger call centers, which can more easily scale up to support an organizational structure to handle it, increased scope pushes the percentage spent on agent labor up. For the largest call centers, experiencing massive economies of scale and great overall efficiencies, labor percentages can rise to the 70, 80, and even 90 percent mark. This happens because of the ability to spread other costs over more agents.

Call Center Size

Given these two examples, one might conclude that larger call centers are ideal. After all, with increased size comes increased call occupancy rates and greater efficiency (that is, increased labor percentages and correspondingly decreased overhead percentages). There are, however, significant downsides experienced in the larger call center, including increased management and control issues, along with far greater complexity.

Therefore, when asked how to determine the ideal call center size, just as with ascertaining the ideal occupancy or labor rate, I can unequivocally state, "it all depends."

Tracking the Wrong Thing

The Risk of Focusing on Misguided Objectives

Y ou may have realized from the past few chapters that I'm a numbers guy. I like to look at statistics and track trends. I enjoy making spreadsheets, calculating ratios, and viewing time-sequenced facts graphically. It's great fun—but a total waste of time if you're tracking the wrong thing.

A case in point is the owner of a midsize medical answering service who boasted that his labor cost was down to 28 percent. He was seeking affirmation for his results, which he had worked hard to achieve for several years. As gently as I could, I informed him that a labor rate of 28 percent implied his overhead was 72 percent. This would suggest that his answering service had a bloated overhead, needing immediate attention to bring it under control. He received my message but didn't appreciate it.

The truth is that when answering service managers focus on labor percentages, they're often looking at the wrong thing for the wrong reason. Yes, unchecked labor costs can quickly escalate, threatening to run out of control. Skyrocketing agent expense is often the most probable cause of the fiscal demise of a call center. On the other hand, too aggressively reducing labor costs is the most common cause of the demise of call center quality.

We need a balance between cost and quality.

If it becomes out of balance, customer service is sacrificed on the altar of cost-containment. For the sake of illustration, let's fabricate a fictitious, yet nonetheless realistic, typical midsize medical answering service (the concepts apply to any call center).

The Situation

To keep the math easy, we'll assume that the answering service has annual expenses of one million dollars and spends 50 percent of its budget on agent labor. For simplicity's sake, we'll lump everything else into the broad category of overhead. We justify this assumption because an answering service's labor directly provides the service, and everything else, albeit important, is either ancillary or indirect.

In summary, the answering service's financial picture looks like this:

- Labor: $500,000 (50 percent)
- Overhead: $500,000 (50 percent)
- Total Expenses: $1,000,000 (100 percent)

Therefore, we have a one million dollar answering service that is spending 500,000 dollars (50 percent) on labor and 500,000 dollars on overhead. To ensure profitability, management has determined to reduce costs by 10 percent. Now what?

Scenario 1

According to conventional wisdom, you address the biggest cost area, which is usually agent labor. Additionally, labor is a variable expense, which means it's easier to cut (fixed expenses are much harder to scale back). In addition, the effects of labor adjustments will quickly be seen, whereas reductions in non-labor-related expenses take longer to materialize.

In any agent schedule, there will be some gray areas. These include the number of agents required at specific times and the length of certain shifts. Even after eliminating these disputable items, there's still considerable, and painful, cutting to do. Eventually, the sagacious scheduler will make the required cuts, resulting in the targeted goal of a 10 percent reduction. The annualized results look like this:

- Labor: $400,000 (44 percent)
- Overhead: $500,000 (56 percent)
- Total Expenses: $900,000 (100 percent)

With the targeted 10 percent cost reduction accomplished and profitability returned, surely things are good, right? Not necessarily. The cutting occurred by solely attacking agent labor. Since the overhead remained unchanged, agent labor received a 20 percent reduction. This will produce a noticeable drop in customer service levels, both measurably by the call center and perceptibly by the callers. An increase in complaints will result, adding work for supervisors and managers, while further taxing the agents, who are now working even harder. It's also likely that some clients will cancel service, causing income to fall and decreasing some of the newfound profits. This scenario exemplifies the old saying of "winning the battle but losing the war."

To extend this unwise scenario, achieving the overly ambitious goal of 28 percent labor cost would require reducing agent labor an additional 205,556 dollars. This would result in:

- Labor: $194,444 (28 percent)
- Overhead: $500,000 (72 percent)
- Total Expenses: $694,444 (100 percent)

Scenario 2

The prudent manager realizes that the answering service's carefully devised schedule is as correct as possible. The agents (labor expense) are the main factor in determining the quality of service offered and the resulting client satisfaction. Once verifying an appropriate agent schedule, the cost reduction efforts should focus on overhead—that is, those activities that do not directly affect the provision of quality service.

It's noteworthy that while agent labor receives constant monitoring and much scrutiny, overhead—or non-agent expenses—tends to receive much less attention. Therefore, inflated expenses are more likely to occur in these areas. This is not to suggest that cutting overhead will be easy. It won't.

It will be difficult, especially since these reductions reside much closer to upper management. Has unneeded fluff crept in? You can cut it without a detrimental effect on service. Likewise, some expenses may no longer be necessary, yet they continue unabated. Other costs, left unchecked, have escalated over time, needing to be trimmed to an appropriate level.

Last, there is a labor component in the overhead category as well. This applies to management at all levels and support personnel. It could be that a certain position is unneeded but retained because everyone likes the person in that position. Other jobs become bloated with unnecessary effort or busywork that produces no real benefit. Bureaucracy and self-preservation activities are also prime targets for elimination. Finally, there is the possibility that complete departments or management levels might warrant elimination.

These types of cost reductions aren't easy to make and are often harder to spot. However, they can happen with the least impact on the callers—the reason that the answering service exists. Reducing costs, other than agent labor, doesn't directly impact the provision of service. The annualized numbers now become:

- Labor: $500,000 (56 percent)
- Overhead: $400,000 (44 percent)
- Total Expenses: $900,000 (100 percent)

The Other Extreme

In the first scenario, we looked at reducing the labor percentage. Cutting labor by 100,000 dollars, and then by another 205,000 dollars, produced a 28 percent labor figure. There is, however, another way to accomplish this same target. Quite simply, holding agent labor constant and increasing overhead by 780,000 dollars will achieve a 28 percent labor figure.

- Labor: $500,000 (28 percent)

- Overhead: $1,285,714 (72 percent)
- Total Expenses: $1,785,714 (100 percent)

This, of course, is a ludicrous example, but it's most illustrative.

Conclusion

There are two ways to reach a 28 percent labor figure: detrimentally slashing labor or obscenely increasing overhead. However, this targets the wrong metric for the wrong reason.

Instead, the intent should be to establish an agent schedule that will produce the proper service level to callers and then shrink overhead to a minimal level. This will effectively increase the labor percentage, while decreasing the overhead percentage—a right and worthy goal for any call center to pursue.

PART 2:

STAFFING

Frontline Staff Is Key to Differentiate Your Operation and Achieve the Results That Patients—and Administrators—Expect

If management is the foundation of the call center, staffing is the cornerstone. Without the right people on the front lines and the necessary support staff behind them, nothing else that the call center does matters, not really.

Though staffing is the single greatest expense in call centers, we're wrong to view it as a cost to control. Instead, it's an asset to treasure and develop.

The chapters in this section will help move us in that direction.

Ideas to Better Retain Call Center Staff

Instead of Hiring New Employees, Strive to Retain
the Ones You Have

I t's becoming increasingly harder to find qualified employees to work in healthcare call centers. This makes it even more important to take steps to retain the employees we already have.

Here are six areas to consider. While these ideas are nothing new, perhaps this chapter will offer a fresh perspective.

Today's workers seek core traits when they evaluate a position and their long-term commitment to it and the organization. Here are the essentials to retain healthcare call center staff:

Compensation

Appropriate agent compensation is a challenge most call centers face. At the risk of oversimplification, if you want to attract higher skilled, more committed workers, you'll need to pay more. Just be sure that when you raise your starting rate, you raise your hiring expectations too.

Benefits

Today's workers want more than money; they seek benefits as well. This includes flexible hours and paid time off. Even part-timers want to go on vacation. Make sure you provide a way for them to do so.

Offer them a retirement plan. Not all will take it, but for future-focused employees, this makes a dramatic difference.

But the big kicker in benefits is healthcare coverage. Being in the healthcare industry, you should have the inside track on how to address this.

Learning Opportunities

Employees also want to learn new skills in their job. Yes, in some cases the training you provide will help their next employer more than you. But for those you retain, you're more likely to realize the benefits of their additional training.

Growth Potential

As your staff learns more job-related skills, they'll want the opportunity to apply them. They want to see the potential for growth, both within their existing position and in any advancement opportunities. Help them see that they have a future with your organization—be it in your call center or another department—and show them how they can get there. This will help them stick around.

If sending your call center staff to other parts of your organization frightens you, remember that each employee you send out into the greater organization has the potential to be an advocate for your call center operation and the important work you do.

Make a Difference

Increasingly, employees care about making a difference at work. Yes, every call provides an opportunity for your call center staff to have an impact, but employees may sometimes feel their work isn't accomplishing anything significant. Help them see the ways they can make a difference on every call, during every shift, and throughout every week.

Besides making a difference within their job, consider ways employees can have influence in their community. Look for a nonprofit organization that you can come alongside and help. Then provide ways for your employees to join in and contribute their time and their skills.

Allow Working from Home

Though not every employee is a viable candidate to work from home, many are. Sending the right employees home to work can result in higher productivity, improved outcomes, and greater staff retention.

Though certain times may mandate that all call center employees work from home, the ideal application is that home-based employment serves as a reward. Make this available to the best employees with a proven record of performance.

Action Step

As you move forward in this initiative to retain call center staff, consider shifting some of your hiring and training budget into the area of retention. Yes, it will take time to realize the results, but when done wisely you'll eventually see your hiring and training costs decrease as you watch your retention rate increase. And who doesn't want that?

We'll expand on these ideas in the next several chapters.

Take a Fresh Look at Agent Compensation

Don't Brush Aside the Importance of Providing Appropriate Call Center Agent Pay

The first of our six ideas to better retain call center staff is to evaluate compensation, a topic of great concern for managers and a critical consideration for agents.

Because of its complexities, it's all too easy for managers to shrug and say, "We're doing the best we can. We can't afford to pay anything more." In fact, I've shared this sentiment with call center staff a time or two myself.

Survey Your Local Market

Several years ago, I consulted for a county medical bureau's answering service. As I met with the call center agents, each one had the same complaint: "People working fast-food make more than we do." After two days of repeatedly hearing this grievance, I did some research. I walked into the eight closest fast-food restaurants and asked what their starting wage was. Each one paid less, often considerably less, than the answering service.

Armed with this information, I set about correcting the agents' unchallenged misconceptions about their pay. My research approach was a quick and easy one, and you may want to do a more thorough analysis, but the point is to survey your local job market to know where you stand. Then you can make informed decisions about what you should pay your agents.

Establish Your Compensation Paradigms

Another answering service I consulted for paid their agents the same as the local fast-food restaurants, which hovered near minimum wage. I told the owner, "When you pay fast-food rates, you get fast-food mentality."

This isn't to criticize fast-food workers (some of them do their jobs with excellence). But taking an order for a hamburger isn't on a par with handling a phone call at 3 a.m. from a hysterical first-time mom concerned about her screaming baby's fever.

Decide what you want your call center agents to make in comparison to other area jobs. Remove the concern about what you can afford and instead focus on what you should aim for. Work to achieve your goal over time.

Make Expectations Match Compensation

At this point, I doubt you've decided you're paying too much. Though you could have concluded you're paying your agents an appropriate hourly rate, you more likely determined that, ideally, you want to pay them more.

But don't make the mistake of increasing your starting hourly pay without making a matching adjustment to your screening processes, employee expectations, and desired outcomes. Pay more and expect more.

Action Step

Making a meaningful change to agent compensation is one of the most terrifying decisions to consider when running a call center. Trying to make huge adjustments too quickly could produce devastating consequences.

Instead, determine where you want to go, plan how to get there, and implement it with care. Over time, make incremental changes to what you pay, what you expect, and what you get in return from your staff.

As you do, you will improve agent retention and increase quality, along with enhancing your employees' attitudes and the workplace environment.

The Fast-Food Factor

Does Your Call Center Have a Drive-Through
Restaurant Mentality?

I've never met anyone who felt their pay was too high. Occasionally, someone will admit to receiving adequate compensation, but most people say their pay doesn't reflect their work or value to the organization. This is especially true of call center agents. I've seen this both while running call centers and as a consultant. It doesn't matter what the pay rate is, the universal belief is that it's too low.

Compensation is the single greatest expense for call centers. It accounts for anywhere from 40 percent to 85 percent of total expenses, depending on call center size. Pay too little, and turnover shoots up, training costs increase, and morale decreases. Pay too much, and the outflow of money exceeds your budget (or the inflow of cash). No organization can stay in business if it loses money every month.

But what is an appropriate pay rate? Fortunately, the answer is close to home. I call it the *fast-food factor*. This is not to denigrate fast-food employees but to acknowledge an all-too-common reality.

Quite simply, if you hire call center agents at a fast-food wage, you'll get a fast-food mentality and fast-food performance. Yes, you'll find the occasional star employee, but how long do you expect to retain them?

Instead, you'll mostly find people with little work experience. They'll view the job as temporary, not understand customer service, and fail to comprehend the necessity of being at work on time, much less giving two weeks' notice before quitting.

Though not every entry-level employee is like this—and there are notable exceptions—too many are. With the average agent training time exceeding the average fast-food employee tenure, you can't afford to hire agents who might quit before they finish training. Yet when you compete with fast-food restaurants for entry-level employees, this is the expected outcome.

To succeed, call centers must pay more than fast-food restaurants, but how much more? Even fifty cents an hour can be effective. A dollar more will have a much greater effect—if you do it right. What you must avoid when raising your starting wage, however, is merely making it easier to find the same caliber of people. You must raise your standards too.

When you pay more, you can expect more.

As covered in the last chapter, the staff at one medical call center kept complaining about their pay. I visited the fast-food restaurants within walking distance of the center. The staff's perception was wrong, but the misinformation had gone unchallenged and was repeated so often that they accepted the lie as truth.

Another client's agents enjoyed a much higher starting wage, but they, too, complained about being under-compensated. Again, I surveyed the pay at nearby fast-food restaurants and discovered the call center's starting wage was three dollars higher than the local fast-food benchmark. Fortunately, accompanying this higher starting wage were tighter pre-employment screenings and higher performance expectations. The caliber of the staff was noticeably greater. In this case, their hourly pay seemed right.

To determine the appropriate hourly rate for your call center agents, you have four options:

1. Continue what you're doing.
2. Pay someone thousands of dollars to conduct a formal wage study.
3. Refer to local wage surveys (which seldom list data for call center agents).
4. Visit local fast-food restaurants, and then distinguish your hourly rate—and agent expectations—from theirs.

Applying the fast-food factor has never let me down and, I suspect, it won't let you down either.

Provide Meaningful Agent Benefits to Improve Agent Retention

Spend More on Retaining Staff and Less on Hiring and Training Their Replacements

The second of our six ideas to better retain call center staff is re-evaluating benefits. This is because pay rate alone isn't enough to keep most call center agents happy and employed.

As we've mentioned, today's workers expect more than decent pay. They want benefits too. This includes part-timers. Yes, your part-timers want—and deserve—benefits. If you want to keep them, you had better provide what they want.

Paid Vacation

Your agents work hard for you and your callers. They deserve a vacation, which gives them a break from the routine of work, provides something for them to look forward to, and helps them recharge. A paid vacation is a prime benefit employees seek. Be sure to provide it to them, both full-time staff and part-timers.

As with all benefits for part-time agents, make vacation pay proportional to the average amount of time they work. For example, if they work twenty hours a week, their vacation pay should be based on a twenty-hour workweek.

Paid Time Off

Next, consider paid time off. This includes sick days and personal days. Ideally, everyone wants healthy employees who don't get sick and who schedule their appointments on their days off. But this isn't always feasible. Failing to provide paid time off could result in an agent coming into work sick or not attending to some important personal issue, which could have negative consequences later.

Retirement

Though not every employee thinks about retirement, some do, and it's important to them. They want to take control of what their retirement looks like, and that means planning for it now, regardless of how far away it is. Be sure to offer them the option to set money aside now for their retirement.

Continuing Education

Next up is the ability to pursue ongoing education. As with retirement, this isn't a benefit that most people seek, but for those who want it, it could make the difference between them quitting or staying.

Tailor your program so that it provides value to participants, as well as to your organization. Also include reasonable precautions to avoid employees misusing or abusing the program, but be fair too. An employee with the opportunity to learn more will provide more value to your organization and be more loyal.

Healthcare Coverage

The last significant benefit is healthcare coverage. Healthcare coverage is a growing concern for people in the United States, with costs rising and coverage shrinking. Yet, being in the healthcare industry, you're in the unique position to help your agents with decent healthcare coverage, or at least you should be.

We'll cover more about this in the next chapter.

Act Now

When it comes to retaining call center staff, don't skimp on benefits. Offer employees paid vacation and time off, retirement and continuing education options, and healthcare coverage. This will increase their loyalty to your organization and decrease the likelihood of them leaving your call center for another company that provides these benefits.

As with compensation, the cost of providing benefits concerns most managers. The key is to offer what you can without jeopardizing your organization. But if you think you can't afford to offer benefits, the reality is that you can't afford not to.

What Kind of Healthcare Coverage Do You Provide to Your Staff?

Take Steps to Meet the Healthcare Needs of Your Healthcare Call Center Employees

I enjoy going to the zoo with my family. We visit several times each year and sometimes we have opportunities to interact with the zookeepers and learn more about the animals under their care. During one visit we had the privilege of an extended discussion with one of the caretakers after she tended to the zoo's three lions.

She shared insider information about their feeding, their training, and their healthcare. After covering the extensive medical care these three amazing animals receive—testing, monitoring, medication, and access to specialists—she grew somber. "They get much better healthcare than I do." We sadly nodded. Then she perked up and resumed telling us about these animals that she so clearly loves.

I wonder if a similar thing happens at healthcare call centers. Do employees hang up from a phone call and shake their heads in dismay, muttering "That caller gets way better healthcare than I do"? I hope not, but I fear it's true far more often than it's not.

It may be understandable for this to happen occasionally, but it's inexcusable if it happens often. This needs to change. Take steps to better meet the healthcare needs of your call center staff.

To expect workers in healthcare call centers to serve patients and callers with excellence, they must first have a good perspective to work from. This includes providing workers with adequate healthcare coverage and services.

Falling short of doing so handicaps them from performing their jobs with distinction and serving callers with appropriate empathy. It would be like making restaurant staff work on an empty stomach and expecting it to not impact patron experience.

Call centers invest money in ongoing agent training, coaching, and quality assurance programs. Make sure to also invest in call center staff's healthcare. This will help ensure that they better connect with the people they talk to on the phone, without negativity and resentment showing through.

If you find yourself needing to make changes, you may not be able to fix everything all at once. But you can move in that direction. Start today.

Offer Learning Opportunities to Better Retain Staff

Everyone Wins When You Provide Strategic Training for Your Staff

To better retain call center staff, we've looked at compensation and benefits. Now we're going to consider learning opportunities.

Today's entry-level workforce values jobs that allow them to grow as individuals. Educational opportunities provided at work or through work help to better connect employees with the job they do, increase their job satisfaction, and lengthen their tenure.

Not only are learning opportunities a wise retention tactic, they're also a smart recruitment tool. Many workers so value learning opportunities that they'll take a lesser-paying job if it provides the chance for them to grow, versus a higher paying position that doesn't.

Here are some learning opportunities you can offer to your staff.

In-House Training

Delivering internally produced training to your staff is a cost-effective way to provide the learning opportunities they crave. This can be unstructured teaching offered as needed or more organized educational offerings. The best thing about developing in-house instruction is that you can tailor it to the specific needs of your call center staff.

Possibilities include one-on-one training, classroom scenarios, and management coaching. You don't need to provide all these options or offer them to all employees, but the smart move is to offer some in-house training to those employees you want to keep or groom for promotion.

Local Seminars

More general business training is available at local seminars. These are usually half-day or full-day events and since they're local, there's little expense beyond the registration fee. Not only do these teach important skills your staff can apply to their work, it's also a way to increase their job satisfaction and enhance their self-esteem due to their new knowledge.

Industry Events

Don't forget industry conferences and conventions. These include both those that are healthcare related and those that are call center related. If an event covers both, that's a bonus.

These opportunities, of course, are more expensive. Registration for conferences and conventions carry a higher fee than local seminars. There are also travel costs involved, which can add up. Therefore, reserve attendance at industry events for employees in management or on a management track.

Formal Education

Also consider offering post-high school educational opportunities, usually college courses. Though this can be toward degree fulfillment, a better solution is to focus on encouraging employees to take specific classes that will directly benefit your call center.

If it makes sense, encourage employees to audit classes. Although this won't result in any credentials for them, it will reduce or eliminate the cost of the class.

Share the Experience

After attending a formal seminar, an industry event, or a college class, you may want to ask staff to report what they learned to their coworkers. This could be a written report, verbal presentation, or hands-on demonstration.

This has three benefits. One is that it reinforces what they've learned. The second is that it allows others in your organization to also benefit from it. Third, it enhances employee self-esteem.

Develop a Career Path

To further enhance the value of these learning opportunities, integrate them with a career path for employees you feel have the potential to advance in the organization. This includes those you see in various future supervisory roles, as well as managerial positions and support functions.

When employees see the work potential that awaits them from these learning opportunities, they'll stay with your organization longer and provide increased value while they're there.

Summary

Not only will these learning opportunities lengthen staff retention, but they'll also increase job satisfaction and improve performance. However, most importantly, as you train employees to do more, they become a more valued resource for your healthcare call center.

Retain Staff by Establishing Their Growth Potential

Increase Employee Tenure by Showing Them Their Future with Your Organization

The fourth idea to better retain call center staff is to provide staff with employee job growth and advancement opportunities. Let's dig into this a bit deeper.

When employees learn enhanced work skills, don't leave them frustrated by not providing the opportunity for them to apply what they've learned. Focus on directing them to job-related growth potential within your organization. This keeps them from seeking their own solutions and advancement opportunities somewhere else.

As you do this, you'll show them the possibility for job enhancement, both in their existing position, as well as advancement opportunities. Show them they have a future in your organization and how they can get there. Not only will you retain a valued employee, but you'll prepare them to become a more essential member of your team.

Here are some ways you can provide employee growth options for your staff.

Add Responsibilities

Each time your staff learns a new skill, look for ways to incorporate it into their current position. Often you can do this by adding responsibilities to their existing job. As they have opportunities that their peers don't have, they'll see themselves as more important to your operation.

This will increase their self-esteem, improve their work attitude, and enhance their job satisfaction. All these will combine to increase their tenure with your company.

Expand Scope

As they prove themselves capable by handling more responsibilities, employees may be ready to take on an increased scope to their job. Look for ways they can be a call center agent and something else. This may mean they are an agent and a shift leader, an agent and a backup supervisor, or an agent and a trainer.

Another option is for them to serve on an ad hoc committee or workgroup to consider new software, implement a new procedure, or overhaul the training manual. Though these are short-term assignments, success in these areas prepares the employee to take on more.

Promote to a New Position

Those who prove themselves by taking on more responsibilities and increasing the scope of their job are ready to be considered for advancement opportunities. Note that this could be within the call center or to another position within the company.

Don't be selfish and try to keep your most talented employees to yourself. Each time they advance to other company departments, you'll realize the benefit of having a call center ally who understands what you do and can advocate for you.

Adjust Compensation

Sometimes asking an employee to do additional work falls within their current pay rate. But don't be stingy. Consider when you should offer a raise, add a benefit, or give an incentive.

Failing to do so will result in employees who are overqualified and underpaid. They then become a prime candidate to leave your organization and go somewhere else. Don't make that mistake.

Develop a Career Path

You should develop a career path to help staff see their growth potential within your call center or the greater organization. It's critical, however, to give a realistic timeframe for this to happen.

You don't know when an existing position will open or a new one will emerge. If you don't include timing variability when developing a career path, your most qualified employees will grow impatient and leave if they don't see things happening as quickly as they think they should.

Summary

When talented staff see the growth opportunities in your organization, they're more likely to stick around so they can achieve their potential. Most employees don't want to go through the hassle and invest the time to find a new job—unless you force them into it.

Don't be the manager that causes your best agents to leave. This will hurt your operation and could benefit your competitor.

Today's Employees Want to Make a Difference

Give Staff Opportunities to Make an Impact through Their Work

Today's employees, especially Millennials and, even more so, Gen Z, want a job where they can impact the world. They want to make a difference by having a positive influence on others through their jobs and at their work. This is the fifth idea to better retain call center staff.

Through Each Call

Starting at training, and reinforced on a regular basis, help employees see how each call they take makes a difference. Show them how their work can positively impact both the caller and the person, department, or recipient of the transaction or information. This way they'll have dozens or even hundreds of opportunities each day to make the world a little bit better.

Over the course of a year that's thousands or tens of thousands of small but meaningful positive interactions where they can help impact their world in a positive way. Embrace this reality, and don't let your staff lose sight of it.

In the Work Environment

Beyond each call, provide opportunities for employees to help make their workplace better. This can include serving on an ad hoc committee, assigning them additional tasks that add value, or taking on special assignments to improve their work environment and better serve callers. It's even more beneficial when they can work together as a team to make a difference.

Offer Volunteer Opportunities

Some companies include paid time for employees to volunteer at their favorite nonprofit. In doing so, employees perceive their employer as supporting the causes they value. They appreciate their work more as a result.

Though it may not be feasible for a medical call center to offer this benefit to every entry-level employee, this paid volunteer time could be a reward for senior agents and those who advance in the company.

Even if you can't (or are reluctant to) provide paid time for staff to volunteer, you can still support their favorite nonprofits in other ways. This could be as simple as offering the organization free voicemail service.

Provide Matching Donations

Other businesses will match employee donations to nonprofits, often dollar for dollar. Usually they place a cap on total matching funds, though this may be an unneeded precaution. Still, if you're just starting this program, having a donation cap may be an effective way to test its effectiveness and limit financial risk. You can always remove or increase the cap later.

Some companies have vetted select nonprofits for matching donations, but this restriction could irritate employees if their favorite charity isn't on the list. This oversight could cause them to resent your organization instead of appreciating it.

The key is to join your employees in supporting what they support. When you do, they'll be more supportive of you.

More Than Money

Today's employees want a job that does more than provide income. They want work that helps them impact their community and their world. Give them these opportunities, and they'll give you their dedication.

Plan for Home-Based Agent Success

If You Don't Yet Have a Distributed Workforce, Now Is the Time to Prepare

The sixth and final idea to better retain call center staff is to allow them to work from home. While there are many advantages in implementing home-based agents, rushing to create a distributed workforce without careful planning carries much risk.

Here are some considerations:

Formulate a Clear Policy

At your call center, you either already have agents who work from home or some agents who want to. Regardless, you must have a clear policy to address this. If telecommuting is something you'll allow, specify how and when it can occur, what the expectations are, and how you'll measure results—both qualitatively and quantitatively.

If you don't permit home-based agents, state this too.

A third option is if you'll consider working from home on a case-by-case basis. Provide guidelines to interested employees and establish evaluation criteria to make consistent decisions.

The point is that—regardless of your intention—you have a clear policy, and stick with it. Don't subject employees to inconsistent management or unfair behavior.

Have a Plan and Work the Plan

Once you've established a plan for home-based agents, clearly communicate it and then carefully implement it. Adopting a plan-as-you-go approach will produce an unsettled workforce.

When this happens, even the most conscientious employees will shove their ideals aside and opt for survival instead. And when staff become unsure of their jobs, the best ones will leave first.

Train Managers to Properly Oversee Remote Staff

Many call center managers and supervisors effectively use the management-by-walking-around style of overseeing staff. This is a common method and can be most effective for centralized employees—and most disastrous in a distributed environment, which requires remote management ability.

If you want to have a distributed workforce and your manager can't effectively handle it, then either provide them with the needed training or find a new manager. Don't make employees who work at home suffer because of ineffective management.

Avoid "Us versus Them"

Once staff become physically separated, with some employees located in the call center and others working from home, an *us* versus *them* mentality can quickly emerge. It's easy to overlook remote staff, not out of malice, but simply from carelessness.

Imagine being off-site and receiving a message that there are donuts in the break room or to check the potluck signup sheet posted next to the time clock.

Referring to remote staff as *them* and the local staff as *us,* especially by management, is a staffing disaster waiting to erupt. Instead use *us* to refer to all employees, regardless of location. Reserve *them* to refer to those outside your organization.

Moving Forward

Having a distributed workforce and allowing agents to work from home offers many benefits. But pursuing it without the proper forethought can erase all the advantages.

A bit of careful planning today will result in a better outcome tomorrow.

The Joys of Working at Home

*Embrace a Home Office as an Opportunity for a Better Life
and More Effective Work*

We often talk about call center agents working at home, but what about supervisors and managers? Management can work at home too.

Since 2000, I've worked at home. The benefits are many: no commute time or expense, no dress code, no need to pack a lunch or go out to eat, and no bored coworkers stopping by to chat. Working at home enables me to accomplish much more in less time. Personally, I love it.

For some people, though, working at home presents challenges. Distractions can abound; there's no one to hold them accountable; the refrigerator is readily available when a craving hits; and they can take a nap if they get tired. Some work-at-home employees work in their pajamas. It's also impossible for them to leave work and go home, since they're already there.

Successfully working at home requires self-control. We need discipline to work when we're supposed to (and *not* work when we're *not* supposed to). We must approach each day with the same professionalism we would in an office and say "no" to distractions.

My first office had no windows. My current one does, which sometimes provides distractions. I once watched four bunnies frolic outside—and then blogged about them. Since I was on my own schedule, this diversion was okay. But to do so for an employer who expects me to be working is unacceptable.

Another time a caller said she heard birds. My window was open and though I had tuned out their happy songs, my headset did not. I shut the windows and turned on the air conditioning.

Can you work at home? It's possible to make it a success—if you want to.

Be Sure to Thank Your Staff

*Let Your Call Center Employees Know You
Appreciate Their Work*

As a final consideration, do you let your staff know you appreciate them? I'm sure you would say "yes," but what would *they* say?

I suspect you're already making a list:

- You provide employment, a paycheck, and a decent compensation package.
- You send them an occasional card or note.
- You award a year-end profit share.
- You pay double time for holiday work.
- You give bonuses.

These things are great, but your staff has grown to expect them. These efforts at indicating gratitude, while appreciated, don't convey that you're truly thankful for your staff and the work they do throughout the year. If they're to realize that you appreciate them, you need to find a better way to say "thank you."

I once had a boss who personally gave me my paycheck every week. Though a man of few words, he would hand me my check, look me in the eye, and say "thank you." He did this for all twenty to thirty people in his department, without fail, every pay period.

That was over thirty years ago, but I still remember. Though he was a hard man to figure out and often frustrating to work for, I had no doubt he appreciated my efforts. His periodic, heartfelt *thank you* kept me motivated, even though his management style sometimes vexed me.

If your efforts to thank your staff fail to communicate your appreciation, it's time for a different approach. Why not try handing each employee their paycheck (or paystub if your organization does direct deposit), looking them in the eye, and saying "thank you"? And if your operation is too big or your staff schedule is too varied for you to do this, do it for your direct reports and encourage them to do it for theirs.

Though thanking your staff indirectly throughout the year is a great start, personally thanking them every pay period will make an impression that lasts.

PART 3:

OPERATIONS

Astute call center operations serve all stakeholders well by producing desirable outcomes

Call center operations is the glue that holds everything together. It's the nexus of management and staffing, supported by a worthy infrastructure, which we'll cover in later sections.

Having the right elements in place for a call center establishes the needed foundation, but it doesn't guarantee that the desired outcomes will necessarily result. Operations is where management and staffing come together to produce a well-functioning team.

Read on to gain more insights into how to make this happen.

Is Your Call Center Effective?

Meeting the Essential Elements of a Call Is Just the First Step

It doesn't matter if a call is answered in a modern contact center staffed with a team of trained professionals or by a weary person in a single-phone department. In both cases, patients and callers will evaluate their phone interactions the same way, and they expect the same outcomes. Regardless of the circumstances, they will compare each call with every other call they've made and judge it accordingly.

It doesn't matter who takes the call or the technology behind it. Call effectiveness is what matters most:

The Two Contact Essentials

At a basic level, patients look for two things when they contact you.

First, they want to accomplish their objective, the reason for their call. This may be to schedule an appointment, follow up on test results, or clarify discharge instructions. Or they might be calling because of a medical concern, hoping to talk to a triage nurse or find out if they should head to the ER.

In short, they have a need, they call you, and they expect to complete their objective.

Second, though they may not realize it, patients subconsciously want a positive feeling about the call. Do they perceive that the agent met their need? Are they satisfied with the outcome? Do they sense the agent treated them with respect?

Together, these two characteristics result in effectiveness.

An effective call is a phone interaction that accomplishes the patient's purpose for calling and leaves them feeling pleased with the interaction. Too often, however, contact centers meet callers' objectives but leave them frustrated. From the patients' perspective, these calls are ineffective.

Degrees of Effectiveness

Being effective means addressing the patient's reason for calling and leaving the caller pleased. A rating of "effective" sets the minimum expectations for a call center. This establishes the center's service baseline.

Calls that aren't effective are failures.

This means either failing to meet the callers' objectives or leaving them unsatisfied with the results. Too many organizations run contact centers that are not effective. They give incorrect information and fail to correct errors. Callbacks don't happen and repeated calls occur, with no progress toward resolution.

However, other contact centers offer the other extreme. They start with effectiveness and then offer more. Their staff is professional, accurate, and consistent. They excel at being empathetic with callers, and they aim for first call resolution.

Effectiveness Goal

Whether you have one phone that rarely rings or hundreds of agents taking calls continuously, first ensure you are effective in handling calls. Then strive to offer more. Become everything your callers hope for when they contact you. Then everyone wins.

Should We Switch Our Mindset from Calls to Contacts?

Move From a Phone-Only Mentality to a
Patient-First Perspective

The first issue of *AnswerStat* magazine rolled off the presses in 2003. Since then, much has changed. Call center technology has advanced, customer expectations have expanded, hiring and training practices have evolved, and new service opportunities have emerged. The internet exploded into a global phenomenon that altered everything.

What hasn't changed much is the telephone call. Call centers still answer calls, make calls, and transfer calls. And we still give and receive information over the phone. The telephone is the ubiquitous communication medium, and it's central to the call center, despite the rise in popularity of other channels.

During these years of technological transformation, there was also faxing and paging, but both were insignificant compared to the widespread practice of simply picking up the phone and calling someone to have a two-way conversation in real-time. Not too many people fax anymore, and it's been ages since I've seen a pager. Yet the telephone remains.

But now we also have email, text, and social media. Some call centers have fully embraced these technologies and integrated them into their operations. Others have persisted in focusing only on phone calls.

Yet the pressure remains for such centers to add these newer forms of communication and connection into their call center mix. As a result, the call center becomes the *contact* center. To embrace this multi-channel paradigm, your call center mindset must be about contacts, not calls.

Consider these forms of contact:

Calls: Phone calls represent most contacts in almost every contact center, and they excel in handling them.

Fax: Some healthcare communication still occurs by fax. Though this channel is small, someone needs to oversee it. Why not the contact center?

Pager: Pagers have gone away in most industries, but they still have value in healthcare where reliability, speed, and disaster-adverseness are vital. Contact centers have always excelled at sending pages, and some even manage pager inventory. There's no reason to stop.

Email: Processing secure email is a natural fit for contact centers. They have the network, the internet connection, the computers, and the staff—and the ability to send, receive, forward, and screen email, just as they do with calls.

Text Chat: Text is growing in most sectors. This is one more channel for the healthcare contact center to add to their arsenal.

Social Media: A growing preference for most people of all ages is to interact online with others through social media. Healthcare organizations require someone to monitor all those comments, tweets, and contacts, responding in a timely manner that is professional and accurate.

With the plethora of social media platforms, no organization can utilize them all, yet they must be where their patients are. The task of interacting with these social-media-minded people is ideal for contact centers.

Self-Service: A final consideration is self-service, the preferred option for most people when they have a question or problem. How, you may ask, does self-service become a contact center opportunity? Doesn't self-service subtract from the contact center? Yes, every interaction handled via self-service is one less interaction handled by the contact center. Yet forward-thinking contact center managers see two opportunities.

The first is that contact centers are in the best position to know what issues self-service should address. Poll a group of agents, and the top ten needs for self-service will quickly emerge. The contact center should serve as the advisor for self-service topics. Better yet, the contact center could take the lead role and produce and administer the self-service content.

The second opportunity is providing backup for self-service. Self-service cannot help everyone, every time. The contact center should catch those that self-service drops. As a bonus, these communications, taken in aggregate, then provide fodder for additional self-service content.

Whatever channels your contact center covers, keep in mind that it's not about the technology, it's about the contact.

Do You Provide Contact Options for Your Patients?

Let Patients Determine Their Communication Channel of Preference and Then Use It

H ave you ever had a company ask how you wanted them to contact you?

How well did they do at complying with your request? With one company I asked for email, but they kept calling me. When I reminded them that I preferred email, they switched to that channel. But later, after too many emails failed to make progress, I switched to the telephone, which confused them. In the end, I accomplished my objective but was frustrated with the process.

Another organization asked the same question. Text messaging seemed the way to go, since I envisioned short, succinct communications with them. Though I opted for text, they emailed me instead. In fact, they always emailed. Once when I called and left a message, they emailed me back. Another time I specifically asked for a text to confirm an appointment, but once again, they emailed me. Email is clearly their preferred contact method, even if it isn't mine.

While I applaud these organizations for asking my preference, I criticize them even more for not following through. If you can't comply, you shouldn't ask. That way you don't establish false expectations or cause frustration with your patient or customer.

In considering these two experiences, a few thoughts come to mind, which apply to any contact center that truly has a customer-focused perspective.

Offering Channel Options Is Good

Letting patients and their caregivers select their preferred contact method is a customer-friendly move. It's also a smart idea, given that patients often have options for healthcare providers and are quick to exercise those options if you disappoint or disrespect them.

Not Honoring Channel Requests Is Bad

Not using the channel a patient requests is worse than not offering the option in the first place. If you can't (or won't) contact patients and prospective patients by the method they request, then don't bother to ask.

Not Responding on Any Channel Is Even Worse

Making no effort to contact patients or callers when they request it is the worst possible error to make. Sadly, this mistake happens far too often.

Knowing When to Switch Channels Is Key

Sometimes a preferred channel bogs down communication. When emails or texts go back and forth without resolution, it's time to pick up the phone, but before doing so, make that suggestion through the patient's channel of choice. And if the patient opts to switch channels, make sure their accumulated interaction follows them to the new channel.

Summary

Providing excellent customer service relies on excellent communication, whether it's within the requested channel or if there's a need to move outside of it. But don't just arbitrarily jump channels. The only thing that will accomplish is patient frustration.

Asking people how they want you to contact them is great, providing you follow through. But if you don't do as they request, you're better off not offering it as an option. Conversely, know when it's appropriate to switch channels. And most importantly, always, always follow through.

~

Develop an Ideal Agent Schedule to Maximize Call Center Efficiency and Effectiveness

For Optimum Results Schedule Agents to Meet
Projected Call Traffic

C all centers rely on people—that is, agents—to meet the needs of callers. This requires developing an ideal agent schedule.

Having too many agents results in idle time, with staff on the clock but without enough work to do. This bloats operational costs. From a theoretical standpoint, an overstaffed call center should provide an exceptional level of service, but this doesn't always happen. Sometimes an overstaffed call center loses focus, grows lackadaisical, and provides poor service.

The opposite of overstaffing is not having enough agents. Not only does this cause agent burnout, but it also lengthens hold times and lowers service levels.

The key is to schedule the appropriate number of agents throughout the day to provide a suitable level of service at an acceptable cost. This minimizes complaints from both callers and agents.

Consider these key points when developing an optimum agent schedule.

Balance Staff Needs with Patient Needs

If all your call center agents work eight-hour shifts, I guarantee your schedule needs work. Though their average workload and service level may be acceptable, most of the day they will swing from either working too hard to not having enough to do.

This means moving away from traditional eight-hour shifts and scheduling staff to work when you need them. To accomplish this, you'll need a mixture of full-time and part-time employees, with part-timers usually being predominant. And your full-timers may need to work shorter shifts or longer shifts. This could be a huge culture shift.

Analyze Small Time Increments

If you track call traffic by the day, your scope is too large. One hour is the longest increment you should consider, but quarter hour segments are better, and some call centers even look at six-minute increments (a tenth of an hour). When you analyze traffic in this granular fashion, you'll see predictable rises and dips throughout the day. Overlay your shifts to cover these peaks and miss the valleys.

Consider Historical Data

In most cases, the call traffic from one week will approximate the traffic for the following week. Averaging several consecutive weeks produces an even more accurate projection. You can also look at traffic from one year ago if you have seasonal fluctuations. Last, to staff for

PETER LYLE DEHAAN, PHD

a holiday, consider the historical traffic from that holiday last year or other comparable days. This lets you project traffic demands and develop an accurate agent schedule.

Pursue Incremental Improvement

Hoping to develop one agent schedule that you can repeat each week isn't realistic. Even if traffic doesn't change much, you'll still need to fine-tune it to best align your agents' availability with your patients' calling patterns. Also, most call center traffic trends up or down from one season to the next. Be sure to adjust for it.

Conclusion

Finding your ideal agent schedule is a delicate balance. It's a time-consuming task, but the results of having an ideally staffed call center are worth the effort.

Ten Steps to Successful Call Center Benchmarking

Embark on a Path to Self-Improvement

Benchmarking is the comparison of your call center with statistical results from the norm of industry peers. These numeric measurements, or metrics, can be in the form of financial figures, operational quality and efficiency, human resource efficacy, or anything deemed valuable to the participants. Usually, however, these are operational in nature.

Successful benchmarking follows a progressive path toward a desired outcome.

Measurement is essential to improvement. It is through objective measurement that you can identify your operation's strengths and weaknesses.

1. Start with the Right Perspective

First, there must be a desire to obtain, have, and use the information. If this is lacking, do not proceed.

2. Determine Participation

Next, you need to determine who to invite to take part in the benchmarking process. The basic requirement is for participants to have an interest in the results and a commitment to contribute. Beyond that, it's imperative that all participants are in healthcare and have similar operations. It's also wise to select those using the same call center platform, since operational metrics are hard to reliably compare when their source is different, employing dissimilar statistical standards.

Some will assert that, from the caller's perspective, a call center is a call center and therefore it doesn't matter what your center is benchmarked with, but it makes no sense to compare your call center to another one that's in a different industry, pursues different goals, or has different cost-benefit standards.

3. Decide What to Measure

The third step is to determine which numbers to collect and compare. Start small, obtaining only a few key metrics. As participants become engaged in the process and realize the value of it, you can add other parameters.

Here are some examples of benchmarking metrics to consider, but remember, start small:

Operational

- Percent of calls answered
- Average time to answer
- Percent of calls placed on hold
- Average hold time
- Occupancy (percent of time spent working)
- Average call duration

- Average wrap-up time
- Number of calls answered per month
- Amount of time spent on calls per month
- Schedule adherence

Human resource

- Annual turnover rate
- Average agent tenure
- Cost to hire one agent
- Cost to train one agent
- Starting pay per hour
- Average hourly rate

Financial

- Cost per call
- Value of the call
- Percent of revenue spent on labor (if applicable)
- Profit margin (if applicable)

4. Standardize Calculations

With the desired metrics in place, develop a standard methodology to gather and calculate the information. Without an agreed-upon procedure, each participant will make the calculation as they see fit, but this will render the results unreliable. Assistance from someone with experience in benchmarking or a background in statistical analysis is helpful, serving to streamline the process. It's even better if this person doesn't have a direct stake in the results, as they'll be more objective in guiding the initiative.

5. Design the Data Collection Form

The fifth step is critical: develop the survey worksheet. This includes documenting the source or calculation of the data. Although this seems simple and straightforward, it's not; a less-than-ideal benchmarking survey form will lead to misanalysis or failure.

Again, someone with experience in benchmarking or developing survey forms will be most helpful.

6. Trial and Tweak

Now, test the survey worksheet. What may seem perfectly clear to those who developed the form could confuse those who use it. Therefore, conduct a small field test. Correct any problems before distributing the benchmark survey to all the participants.

7. Complete the Survey

Although gathering the needed information and filling out the survey form is time-consuming, it should be straightforward if the survey design first underwent appropriate testing.

8. Collect and Analyze the Data

An independent third party should receive and process the completed benchmarking surveys. It's imperative that all participants trust the person who will collect and analyze the data. There must be no perception of a conflict of interest. Select someone who won't benefit from the results.

9. Share Findings

Present the results of the benchmarking survey in aggregate form and then only to those who responded. Fully protect individual answers. In some cases, such as providing cross-sectional or demographic analysis, you may need to eliminate certain sections due to a small number of responses that would expose one or two benchmarking members.

All who participated should receive the results, often along with analysis and a commentary.

10. Fine-Tune and Repeat

Although conducting a benchmarking study once is valuable, the real benefit comes from repeated studies over time. Therefore, it's important to follow up with those who participated to fix any problems or identify additional data to collect.

Make these changes and repeat the survey. Depending on the nature of the information, repeat the survey annually, possibly semiannually, quarterly, or even monthly.

Benchmarking Outcome

The benchmarking results become a periodic report card showing your successes, your shortcomings, your improvements, and your relapses—all with respect to your peers. This provides the basis for celebration and self-improvement.

Healthcare Call Center Lessons from Another Industry

Learn from Customer Service Gone Wrong

When searching for an internet service provider, I entered my address into the website of the most likely supplier. Four service options came up. I clicked the first, which said, "Service not available." I clicked the second: "Service available." They looked like the same service, but the second had more features. The third was likewise not available, while the fourth one was.

I called the sales number, and the agent said, "I'm sorry, but we don't serve your area." I explained what I had found online. He checked again, and then a third time, muttering as he verified the address each time. He finally said, "I guess my system isn't up to date. Let me transfer you to customer service. Even though you're not a customer, they can help."

The person in customer service didn't appreciate that he transferred me to her, since I wasn't a customer. Full of disdain, she assured me that all four options were available. She needed to transfer me to another department, but I never heard what they had to say. She disconnected me instead.

It's not surprising that I called a different provider.

Here are some call center lessons we can learn from this hapless company:

Synchronize Data

Make sure the information available to patients (patient bills, hours of operation, appointment availability, room numbers, and so forth) aligns with what the agents see. Don't send patients to one online resource and agents to a different one that is offline. Although it's appropriate to provide more information to agents, make sure that what the caller can access doesn't contradict what the agent sees.

Avoid Transfers

Strive to resolve calls the first time, by the first agent. Each time an agent transfers a call, risks occur. At a minimum, the caller needs to repeat information they have already shared once—or twice—if they had to also enter data into an IVR (such as a patient ID or invoice number) before talking with the first agent.

I've noticed that the person I'm transferred to is often not able, or is unwilling, to help me. At worst, they're irritated. I've interrupted them and they treat me poorly, which brings us to. . .

Be Nice

The purpose of call center agents is to help patients and callers find answers and solve problems. There is no rule that you must be nice to assist people, but it sure helps.

Agents who are pleasant with callers are more likely to leave those callers with a favorable opinion of the transaction. Giving accurate information with a negative attitude is an example of "winning the battle but losing the war."

In addition, part of being nice is to not disconnect callers.

Train Thoroughly

Make sure agents know how to access all the databases and resources they need to do their job—and that they have the proper login credentials. Train them in product knowledge (classes, promotions, and every new initiative) and processes (such as admissions, discharge, invoicing, and so forth).

If you launch a marketing program, make sure they know about it before the campaign starts. And last, make sure they excel at operating their computer and console, including how to properly transfer callers to the right party without disconnecting them.

Apply these four principles to your healthcare call center and you will serve them well. Isn't that the point?

Call Center Collaboration

Work with Other Organizations to Improve Results and
Maximize Outcomes

During uncertain economic conditions, it's critical for healthcare call centers to explore ways to bolster their revenue stream and ensure their ongoing existence. One option is to collaborate with another call center or health organization for their mutual benefit, such as a medical answering service working with a nurse triage call center. Over the years, I've been involved in many similar alliances, with varying results.

Here are some ways things can go awry:

The Quick Fix

Most collaborations take time to produce results. Expecting an immediate payoff is unrealistic. If you pursue a joint venture as a futile survival effort, it may already be too late to do any good. Instead, seek innovative solutions while there is time to nurture them. The payoff, while not imminent, can be long term.

Unwilling to Contribute

Too often people enter partnership arrangements with the erroneous expectation that with only a little effort they will be able to realize great benefits from the work of the partner company. This is selfish and shortsighted. Even if results initially occur, the partner will have no reason to continue doing all the work while others reap the benefits.

Having a Win-Lose Mentality

Sometimes one or both parties persist in the belief that the only way for them to come out ahead is for their partner to lose. When this occurs, the only possible outcome is that both parties lose.

Taking Advantage of Your Partner

If one party in a joint venture has a hidden agenda, their ruse will eventually become known. The only results will be ill will and a possible lawsuit.

This could occur when one party doesn't want to put forth the needed effort, share relevant data, or allocate resources, but still expects to receive the results produced by the other party.

Inequitable Responsibilities and Rewards

Arrangements where one party consistently expends a greater amount of time and resources while realizing lesser results is a collaboration destined for collapse. Alliances with one participant consistently receiving more benefits than the effort they expend will fail.

Lack of Predetermined Objectives and Measurements

If you don't agree on the target, how will you know if you hit it? How will you determine if the collaboration is working? Stating that your aim is to increase call traffic is vague and untenable. A goal must be specific and quantifiable.

For example, there are different valid ways to measure call traffic. Perhaps one partner wants to track the number of incoming calls, while the other partner wants to chart the number of agent minutes. Both are valid, but they are different. Introducing call automation will affect both measurements, but with opposite outcomes. With automation, calls could increase, while agent minutes plummet.

As a result, one partner is pleased, and the other isn't.

No Exit Plan

It's unwise to assume any collaboration will last forever. Things change. What once was mutually beneficial will one day cease to be. Lacking a clear and defined ending exposes participants to needless confusion or frustration. Suppose one partner needs to buy equipment, purchase inventory, or hire staff for the alliance to endure. If the venture's future is vague, there will be a reluctance to make these investments.

Collaboration Checklist

With these pitfalls in mind, here are some recommendations for how to embark upon a successful collaboration:

- Be forthright about your expectations and contributions.
- Pursue a mutually beneficial relationship.
- Set specific and measurable goals.
- Do your part to ensure success.

- Predetermine a controlled, ethical, and responsible manner to end things with minimal damage to all stakeholders.

Conclusion

While there is much that can go wrong in pursuing a call center collaboration, there is an exciting upside when wisely implemented, such as increased business, enhanced customer service, or a greater market share. Avoiding the preceding pitfalls and pursuing these recommendations positions a collaboration for success.

PART 4:

CUSTOMER SERVICE

The Patients Who Contact Your Call Center Operation
Expect—and Deserve—Great Customer Service

Patients and callers don't compare your healthcare call center with other industry operations. Instead, they compare you with every other call center they've ever contacted across all industries.

That means their call to find a physician, make an appointment, or navigate your organization must match their various experiences with other companies they contact, such as to place an order, correct an invoice, or lodge a complaint.

If you fall short in meeting their expectations—as determined by the greater call center industry—you will disappoint them, damage your organization's mission, and thwart its objectives.

The chapters in this section apply equally to both management and staff. Please share these insights with your charges.

The Perfect Answer

Good or Bad, the First Words We Say on Each Call Makes an Impression

How often have you called someplace and wondered if you reached the right number? All too often, agents answer calls in a rush, carelessly, or incompletely. Or the agent sounds out of breath by the end of a lengthy, tongue-twisting welcome. It's vital to consistently answer all calls in the same way, regardless of location or agent.

Here are three parts to the ideal answer:

Greeting

The greeting serves to set a positive tone for the call. It's a simple "Good morning," "Good afternoon," or "Good evening." The greeting tells the caller someone has answered the phone.

These words signal to the caller that it's time to listen, but it also isn't critical if the caller misses these words.

Provider Identity

This is simply the name of your organization, such as "Acme Medical Call Center." It lets callers know the organization they've reached and confirms their call has gone through correctly.

Say the name as most people outside your organization would best understand it. Drop legal suffixes such an Inc., LLC, and Ltd. Also, avoid abbreviating the company name. Saying "AMCC" when everyone knows you as "Acme Medical Call Center" will only cause confusion.

Agent Identity

The final element is your first name. It adds a valuable personalized touch. It's much easier for a caller to get mad at an anonymous voice than at an identified person. Using your name builds rapport and establishes a connection with the caller. As the last word of the answer phrase, it is also the one most easily remembered.

Omitting your name implies an avoidance of personal involvement. Ending with your name signals confidence and competence, which are critical in medical call centers.

Avoid Unnecessary Addendums

It is all too common for people to tack on the inane phrase, "How may I direct your call?" A direct response to this senseless question would be "quickly and accurately." This is a waste of time.

Putting these three elements together results in the perfect answer:

"Good morning, Acme Medical Call Center, this is Peter."

Please Hold While I Disconnect You

Learn to Transfer Calls with Excellence

The rate of success in transferring calls is often poor. Based on my experience, successful transfers occur less than half the time. Even if my call isn't outright disconnected, there are problems with being transferred to the wrong extension or put on endless hold.

To help, here are some commonsense, but often overlooked, steps:

Training

Cover the proper transfer procedure in training. Have the trainee experience transfers from the perspective of the caller and the recipient as well as the agent. Doing so gives them a better understanding of how errors occur and affect others.

Practice

To master any skill, practice it until it becomes second nature. For agents who don't frequently transfer calls, ongoing practice is advisable.

Consistency

Most systems provide multiple ways to transfer calls. Pick the most universally applicable method and teach it to all agents. Have trainers use this standard method and no others. Then discourage agents from using other processes or shortcuts.

Methodology

Pick one call-transferring philosophy:

- **Blind Transfer:** A blind transfer is the quickest, but least professional, option. To do this, the agent dials the number, connects the caller, and hangs up before the called party answers.
- **Announced Transfer:** In an announced transfer, the agent dials the number, tells the recipient about the call, connects the caller, and hangs up.
- **Confirmed Transfer:** A confirmed transfer goes one step further than an announced transfer, in which the agent stays connected just long enough to ensure that the recipient can address the caller's needs. If the recipient is unable to assist the caller, the first agent takes control of the call and seeks a different recipient.

Verify

Periodically check transfer lists by physically dialing them. Frequent verification is the only way to purge wrong numbers and ensure accurate information for the agents.

First Call Resolution

If you pursue first call resolution, you reduce the need to transfer callers, even eliminating it altogether. This is the best solution of all.

Who Signs Your Paycheck?

Knowing Who You Work for Helps You Do a Better Job

D o you know who signs your paycheck? This, of course, is a theoretical question, because most workers today receive their compensation electronically, without knowing who authorized the transfer.

When I ask who signs your paycheck, however, I don't mean in a literal sense but in a broader, holistic way. That is, who is responsible for the money you make? Who do you work for? Let's consider the options:

Your Employer

First on the list is the company you work for, your employer. They hired you, trained you, and pay you for your work. Regardless of the size of the organization you work for, however, there are numerous facets to employment.

First is your boss, and the managers and supervisors they have in place to oversee your work. Larger organizations have a hierarchy. There is your boss's boss and even their boss. There could be officers and a board of directors. A corporation has stockholders who own the company. You work for them all. In effect, each one signs your paycheck.

What about your coworkers? In a well-functioning organization, everyone works together to meet a common goal: serving patients. And if you're in a position of authority, you have people working under you. In a way, you work for them too, by providing support, encouragement, and direction. If they succeed in their jobs, you succeed in yours.

Your Clients

If you're employed in an outsource call center, where you handle calls for other companies, you work for them too. Serve them well to retain their business, and you will continue to have a job. Serve them poorly, and they'll cancel service. If this happens too often, your future employment is at risk. In this way, you work for your clients as much as you work for your employer.

Your Callers

Regardless of the type of call center you're in, you work for your callers too. Without them, you'd have nothing to do. They're critical to your ongoing employment.

Though most people who work in call centers desire to do their best to help others, not everyone is so service-oriented. Do your best to take care of callers, which is what your company hired you to do.

You

In addition to your employer, clients, and callers, you also work for yourself. You work to earn a living. You may also want to make a difference through your job.

You can best do this by handling calls with excellence.

Conclusion

In practice, you don't work for one person, but for many. All of them, in their own way, sign your paycheck. Though there's an obvious priority, strive to give your best work to each one of them, including yourself.

Don't let this thought of working for everyone overwhelm you. Instead, let it motivate you to give your best to your job every day, on every call.

Serve Your Stakeholders

Understand Your Purpose in Working at a
Healthcare Call Center

You work in a healthcare call center. Why? The most basic answer is to receive a paycheck so you can pay your bills. Though this is an essential motivation, earning a living will only take you so far in your call center work—and your career.

To find fulfillment, you must move beyond a paycheck to embrace the purpose of the call center. Why are you there? To serve your stakeholders—all of them.

Callers

The most obvious on the list of stakeholders are the patients who call you. They have a need, and they hope you can meet that need. When you do, you end up making their life a little bit better. They end the call glad to have talked with you and appreciative of what you did for them.

But when you fall short of helping them achieve their goal, you cause frustration. They hang up exasperated.

Although you won't win with every call, you should strive to succeed as often as possible. Meeting the needs of callers and patients is the first way to serve your stakeholders.

Coworkers

Your coworkers are also stakeholders, albeit an often-overlooked group.

As you serve callers, you do so within a team environment. Are you a team player? Do your coworkers view your presence as an asset or a liability? Make sure your colleagues can count on you to do your part and not cause more work for them.

In fact, do more than what's expected whenever possible to help make your associates' jobs easier. Don't be the person who blasts through the day without regard to the people who work around you. Instead, aim to be the person everyone wants to sit next to.

Boss

Whatever position you fill in your healthcare call center, you have a boss—often more than one. Your bosses are also stakeholders. By serving callers with excellence and getting along well with your colleagues, you've taken the first two steps in being the employee every manager wants to have. Now look for ways you can do more to make your boss's job easier or lighten the load they carry in your call center.

Community

A fourth stakeholder to consider is your local community. By doing your job well, you play a part in making society better. As you address the healthcare needs of your callers, you elevate the overall health of the area you live in.

Don't lose sight of the fact that the work you do benefits your neighbors and community.

Organization

Whether a corporation or a nonprofit, the organization you work for is an essential stakeholder. It provides the infrastructure for you to work in and the means to pay you and provide benefits. As your organization succeeds, you will be the better for it. But if your organization struggles—especially if you could have helped realize a different outcome—you'll experience the same fate.

Though no organization is perfect in all it does, do what you can to help yours become the best it can. This not only occurs on every phone call you take but also in the space between them.

Conclusion

Don't be an employee who just shows up to collect a paycheck. Be an asset to your organization and serve your stakeholders—all of them—with excellence. This includes your callers, your coworkers, your boss, your community, and your organization.

Are You Changeable?

Understanding Change is the First Step to Dealing
with It in a Positive Way

If the only constant is change, why is change so hard? Call centers, especially those in the healthcare industry, go through frequent changes, perhaps more so now than ever before. These changes might include merging operations, moving locations, implementing revised procedures, adjusting to new regulations, or updating equipment or software.

Regardless of the reason, three universal truisms exist: change is opposed, change is viewed as loss, and change is mourned.

1. Change Is Opposed

Change represents a deviation from the status quo, from what people expect, whether good or bad. Change moves from the known to the unknown. Therefore, it is normal that people will oppose change, resisting it to whatever degree they can. This might mean clinging to old ways, lobbying against the change, or rebelling by acting out, offering resistance, or engaging in passive-aggressive behavior.

2. Change Is Viewed as Loss

Change implicitly means giving something up—even if it's something bad. Many people view change as a "zero-sum game," assuming that there are winners and losers. They assume that if the change makers have won, then they've lost. This assessment is natural and expected, especially if the change was not their idea.

3. Change Is Mourned

When losing something to change, it's lamented and grieved. Sometimes the loss is merely perceived (it didn't happen) or potential (it might happen), whereas other times it is actual (it did happen).

Regardless, the emotional reaction to that loss is mourning. Just as there are steps to grieving (be it five, seven, or ten, depending on which list you consult), mourning the loss wrought by change will progress down a similar path—and take time.

The Recommended Solution

However, it doesn't need to be this way. People can better accept change if it's understood, occurs in small increments, and is within the control of those affected by it. This trio of suggestions may not offer much relief when confronted with global or national upheaval, but the suggestions are helpful when responding to changes in your personal and work lives, such as in the call center.

In these circumstances, managers can make reasonable efforts for their charges to accept, and even embrace, change.

1. Change That's Understood

Change can best be accepted and dealt with when it's understood by those most affected. This doesn't necessitate agreeing with the change, but merely comprehending the decision behind it. To accomplish this, forthright communication is key: not just once, but repeatedly. Also, provide as much notice before a change as possible, giving those affected more time to process and grasp the change.

2. Change in Small Increments

Whenever possible, divide the change into segments and space them out over time. Change made gradually and in small doses has a much better chance of acceptance and success. It becomes more manageable for those leading it and more tolerated by those affected.

3. Change Within the Control of Those Affected

Whenever people can experience some degree of control over change, they're more likely to handle it positively. If possible, let those affected provide input or even choose when the change will occur, the pace of the transition, or how training will transpire. While they will have little control over the outcome, they can exercise control over the path to get there.

Change Summary

Yes, people tend to oppose change, view it as loss, and mourn it, but astute managers can minimize these normal responses by clearly communicating the reasons for the change, making the change gradually in small increments, and providing as much control as feasible to those most affected.

This won't avoid the change, but it can alleviate many of the negative reactions to it.

Does Your Call Center Amaze or Annoy?

*Wow Callers with Your Work and Don't
Needlessly Irritate Them*

Whenever I make a phone call, I scrutinize what happens; it's an occupational hazard. Often what I witness provides fodder for a column or blog post. So, based on personal experience, here are some ways you can either amaze or annoy your patients and callers:

Interactive Voice Response

Most people hate IVR, likely because of poor implementation. Though IVR can be great if it speeds up calls, I have doubts about that happening. Once I made repeated calls to a help desk, each time navigating seven levels of prompts, which took almost two minutes per call. Unfortunately, the person who eventually answered could never help me and had to transfer me to someone else. Worse are endless IVR loops, forcing callers to hang up or make a wrong selection to escape.

If your call center has IVR, make sure it speeds up calls from a caller's perspective. Remember, you're there to serve them. And always provide the option to press zero for an agent. Just make sure to route it to a person and not back to the beginning of the IVR tree or into an unidentified voicemail.

Estimated Wait Time

Informing callers of the expected time before an agent will be available is a nice touch. Usually the estimate is accurate, and often the agent answers sooner.

My worst experience was being "next in line," a promise that repeated every fifteen seconds. After thirty minutes, I placed the call on hold and ate dinner. I returned to hear the same announcement and waited another two hours. I put the call on hold again and went to bed. After fourteen hours, I was still "next in line." I placed a second simultaneous call and that one was also "next in line." I disconnected both calls and redialed; I was still "next in line."

After waiting another two hours of being "next in line," someone responded to one of my many email pleas for help. It was the president of the company, and he was not pleased to hear about my ordeal.

It's great to offer this customer-friendly feature; just periodically test it to make sure it works.

Schedule a Callback

Having the choice to receive a callback instead of waiting on hold is a nice option, provided the company follows through. Mostly it works as promised, but one time no one ever called me. Another time, I received a callback but on a different number and day than I requested.

While some people are willing to hold for the "next available agent," others prefer the freedom to do something else as they await a return call. Win patient appreciation by offering both.

Once Should Be Enough

After entering information on my keypad to talk to a person, I often need to repeat the same information to an agent, sometimes more than once. This is exasperating and is poor customer service.

Make sure your call center captures requested information and passes it along with the call, from system to system and agent to agent.

Your Number, Please

I expect call centers to know the number I'm calling from and display it to agents, but this commonsense feature is often lacking. Don't ask me for what you should already know.

Also, if you access my account by phone number, make provisions for patients who call from different numbers or change numbers. For one vendor I still need to give them my old phone number that changed several years ago. They can't seem to update their system to handle my new number.

For Further Consideration

Does your call center technology amaze or annoy your patients and callers?

When Human Errors Cost Call Centers More Work

Take Steps to Avoid Miscommunications that Cause Problems for Everyone

I have a love/hate attitude toward downloading monthly statements and invoices. I love receiving the information faster and storing it electronically. But I hate the problems that come up, such as login frustrations, redesigned pages that hide my information, and unavailable statements. And this doesn't just apply to my monthly healthcare statements and summaries. All industries seem equally guilty.

Here's an example:

Misinformation

Once I received an email to download my monthly summary. I logged in but couldn't find the document. I searched and I clicked, and I logged in again. Nothing helped. At the bottom of the page was a link to email them with questions. I concisely shared my frustration and clicked "send."

To my surprise, I received a response within minutes. The agent explained that someone sent the email notice prematurely. "The problem has been corrected and your statement is now available for download."

Wasted Time

I logged in again, but the document was still not available. This time I spotted a toll-free number and called customer support.

The recording said to expect an eighteen-minute wait. I opted to receive a call back when it was my turn. Eleven minutes later, my phone rang, but instead of talking to an agent I heard a recording followed by music while I was on hold. When the agent eventually answered, I explained the situation, making little effort to hide my frustration.

After doing some checking and consulting with someone else, the agent confirmed the initial email went out in error, the agent who handled my follow-up email gave me incorrect information, and my statement still wasn't online.

"When will it be available?"

"I don't know, but legally we have six more days before it must be posted. Just keep checking."

The next day, on my fourth try, my statement was there. I downloaded it, having invested about an hour in total to accomplish this simple task.

The company sent me a brief customer service survey. My snarky comment was, "Don't email me to download my statement before it's actually available." I never received a response.

Extra Customer Service Work

This company sent an email in error, which resulted in me contacting their customer support center and causing them one needless activity. To compound the problem, the agent provided me with incorrect information. This caused the company a second needless activity. And assuming someone looked at my customer service survey, this caused a third needless activity.

Thousands of others received this errant email message too. If only a small percentage contacted the company, how many more needless activities took place?

I'm sure the contact center agents had a difficult, busy day—all courtesy of one person who prematurely sent a mass email message. Sometimes we cause our own problems. And the call center often pays for it.

Provide Memorable Experiences

Call Center Lessons from a Walk-in Healthcare Clinic

I once went to a walk-in healthcare clinic to deal with a rash that turned out to be some variation of poison ivy. Not only did I get fast attention and quick results, but I had a most enjoyable experience. I left the clinic a happy patient, which is the opposite reaction from what I experience after interacting with most healthcare call centers.

Here are some thoughts on how to produce positive interactions, whether in person or over the phone.

Accessible Service

To start, the clinic was brightly lit, easy to find, and offered nearby parking. The relaxing atmosphere gave me assurance I could anticipate a successful outcome.

Too often call centers aren't accessible. They hide their phone number. Why is this? Don't they want calls? By the time I do talk to someone, I'm already doubtful I'll be able to accomplish my objective.

Easy to Use

When I walked in, a check-in kiosk greeted me (along with a medical assistant, who was checking in another patient). I entered my name, punched a couple buttons, and was ready for step two.

Contrast this to a call center, with its endless array of auto-attendant prompts that seldom fit the reason for my call. And if I pick wrong, the best solution is to hang up and start over. Though call centers should be easy to use, the reality is often different.

Known Timeframe

At the healthcare clinic, I immediately knew where I was in the queue by counting the number of patients in the waiting room. And the kiosk provided additional information with an expected wait time of 28 to 56 minutes.

Anticipating this, I had my iPod to keep me company. But before I even plugged in my earbuds, the first patient had been ushered into an examination room, and the man in front of me was already being checked in. In a few minutes he went to exam room two. I was already next in line, and it hadn't even been five minutes.

I always appreciate call centers that tell me where I am in the queue and give me updates as things progress. All healthcare call centers should offer this customer-friendly feature.

Provide Options

I learned I could have checked myself in online. This would have guaranteed my place in the queue at the clinic. Then they would have texted me as my appointment slot neared.

This is much like call centers offering a callback option. It's nice to have alternatives. Why don't more call centers do this?

Exceptional Staff

The most impressive thing was great staff. The medical assistant at the healthcare clinic was both professional and personable. Within seconds she had me checked in. A few minutes later she moved me to exam room one after the first patient left.

This positive experience continued with the physician assistant. She treated me as a person and not as a problem to solve. She was patient, thorough, and precise in her diagnosis and recommendation. I'm looking forward (kind of) to my next visit.

Too often, with the continuous onslaught of calls, call center personnel view each caller as a problem to handle as fast as possible, not as a person who needs help. Making this distinction is key in the overall customer experience.

Successful Results

Less than twenty minutes after I arrived at the healthcare clinic, I left with a credible diagnosis and a prescription to pick up at the pharmacy, which was less than one hundred feet away. This was the outcome I sought.

How often have I hung up with a call center having fallen short of my goal? Sadly, the answer is too often. I may call back for a different rep, phone somewhere else, or just give up.

Skilled Close

Before I left to pick up my prescription, I chatted again with the medical assistant. Though I didn't need to see her afterward, she had more information for me. When she learned I didn't have a primary care physician, she encouraged me to get one and offered to help.

I shared my past frustration at not being able to find someone close by. She took this as a challenge. When I left, she handed me a slip of paper listing four nearby doctors who were accepting new patients. It's too soon to know if she made a successful upsell, but she did an excellent job at doing everything she could to help. I left with a positive feeling.

When done appropriately, an upsell by a call center agent is both helpful and appreciated. But when done poorly, it's an irritant and another reason to not call back. Be sure to end each call well.

The Next Step

How can you apply these observations of a healthcare clinic to make your medical call center a shining example of success that your callers and patients appreciate?

Working with a Health Coach

See Your Work through the Eyes of a Patient

A friend recently switched his healthcare insurance. His new provider declared that his weight was an issue and charged him a premium as a result. His former insurer had done so too, as well as the two before that. Each time he'd shrug his shoulders with a resigned, "Oh, well" attitude.

But this time was different. In addition to the premium bump, his provider assigned him a virtual health coach to help him bring his weight down to an acceptable level. This irritated my friend, who complained about the intrusion and the indignity of being forced to work with a coach.

Though he says his health coach is nice enough, he doesn't like her. I doubt he would like anyone in that role. She calls once a month. If my friend dodges the call, his mentor is persistent. Now he's learned just to answer her call when it comes so he can fulfill his once-a-month obligation.

The health coach offers suggestions, and my friend dismisses them: "Now here's what I'm going to do" is his response.

I ask if his coach offers encouragement. He admits that this might be the case.

"Isn't that what she's supposed to do?" Then I ask, "Do you find her encouragement irritating? Or is she over-the-top perky?"

"No. She's okay. She's just doing what she's supposed to do. It's her job."

He claims to have ignored every suggestion offered. Yet, he's losing weight. After six months he is near his goal. I can see the difference, both in his appearance and in his actions.

"So she must be helping," I say.

"Nope," he insists. "I just increased my physical activity and decreased my portion size. I figured that out on my own."

Once he hits the target weight they assigned to him, the premium drops to normal and the health coach will stop calling. I wonder if he'll keep the weight off.

Moving Forward

Over the telephone, we often don't know how patients regard us or if we're truly helping callers. In the absence of tangible feedback, remain diligent in working, just as you were trained. This is the best way to impact others in a positive way.

PART 5:

MARKETING AND PROMOTION

Whether Your Call Center Is an In-House Operation or an
Outsourcer, Don't Neglect Marketing

For an outsource healthcare call center provider, marketing is an obvious need to obtain new clients and maintain a viable operation. Yet the in-house call center operation also has a need for marketing and promotion. It's just that your marketing initiatives are to a different group of stakeholders.

Regardless of your situation, this section includes chapters to drive successful marketing and promotion initiatives.

Define Your Distinguishing Difference

Discover What Makes Your Call Center Unique

What does your healthcare call center stand for? How do you stand out in an industry with many options? Understanding who you are is the first step to determining your distinctive characteristics. But why does it matter?

This is important because when you have a unique quality your stakeholders have something to rally around. They have a reason to be proud. Short of that, you offer nothing special to draw them in and keep them close. They have nothing to celebrate.

Whether you're an outsource call center or in-house operation, here are some areas to consider.

Service

The first place most call centers look at to distinguish themselves is their level of service. They often focus on quality. Though there are many ways to define this, some look at customer satisfaction (CSAT). Most every call center claims to offer quality service.

However, saying it and doing it are two different things. To trumpet service quality with integrity requires that a third party confirm it. Self-pronounced claims of quality service mean nothing.

Aside from quality, other service considerations might be answering calls quickly (average speed to answer: ASA) or handling requests on one contact (first call resolution: FCR). Other ways to stand out include a low error rate or around-the-clock accessibility.

Staff

A second area to consider is how you relate to your staff. Though few employees say they're overpaid or over appreciated, look at how you regard your staff. Employees who receive proper compensation and know how much they're appreciated tend to work harder and produce better outcomes. The side effect of this is improved service to callers, as well as a healthier financial position.

In call centers, where margins are thin, leaders often struggle with their compensation packages. They know that even a 5 percent increase in payroll can move a profitable (or cash-positive) operation into an unprofitable (or cash-negative) one. Yet others successfully apply the adage of "pay more and expect more."

Not all approaches to enhancing the relationship with your staff, however, require a financial investment. Consider intangible ways to stand out. This includes letting employees know how much you appreciate them, connecting with them on a personal level, and even taking the simple step of giving them a sincere *thank you* for their work.

Finances

A third area to consider is the financial aspect. Is your operation fiscally strong? A call center that produces consistent positive cash flow has long-term viability. This means they generate profits for their owners or are a profit center for their organization. Having financial stability can permeate an entire operation with positivity.

Resources and Tools

Fourth, do you provide your staff with the best tools possible? Is their work environment something they're proud to enter every day? Though this may not seem like a relevant consideration to use to define your call center, employees in a top-notch work environment will speak highly of their jobs and their employer to their families and friends. This can ripple through the local area, elevating the call center in the process.

Moving Forward

Though it's good to address all these areas and strive to make them the best you can, it's impossible to make everything a priority. Attempting to do all things well at the same time will cause all areas to suffer.

Without neglecting any of these considerations, however, strive to elevate one above all others. Let this become the distinctive characteristic for which your call center is known and celebrated. This will help you stand out among all others and have a lasting impact for all stakeholders: your callers, your employees, and your organization.

Knowing what makes your call center stand out is a prerequisite for marketing, regardless of who you're marketing to or why.

Rebranding a Medical Call Center

A Label Is Only as Good as the Organization and
Staff behind It

Recently, a company I do business with announced a name change. They're rebranding themselves. Their new name is supposed to better align with their core values, culture, and corporate vision. It's also intended to dispel some of the misunderstandings associated with their current name.

I understand this, and yet I think it's a mistake. They're going to lose a lot of momentum and confuse people in the process.

While it's fun to dream, plan, and think great thoughts about rebranding, it's more important to serve patients with excellence and provide value for the money they spend with your organization. Although a brand can help accomplish these things, it can also serve as a distraction.

If you're thinking about rebranding your call center—be it your name, your market identity, or your vision—here are some things to consider.

What's in a Label?

One big issue in rebranding is the label of *call center*. It may be that these two words are part of your name or at least implied by it. They may appear on your website and be part of your promotional materials. Yet, for many people, the phrase *call center* carries negative connotations and bad memories.

As a result, some call centers think they need to distance themselves from this label. The label of contact center is one replacement. Others include customer service department or communication center. Additional concerns about a name include finding one that better describes what you do now and doesn't limit you in the future.

But will changing your name really accomplish anything?

What's behind the Label?

Let's say you stop referring to yourself as a call center and switch to contact center. You do take more than calls; you handle contacts. But what will this name switch affect? If you continue offering the same types of service, with the same degree of quality, and with the same staff, nothing has changed. Not really.

The reason the label *call center* holds negative connotations for much of the public is because of frustrating experiences they've had when they've interacted with them. If you start calling yourself a contact center—or implement any other label change—without first making underlying improvements, you run the risk of simply transferring people's negative image of your existing brand to your new brand.

The rebrand won't mean much if the change is nonexistent or superficial. Changing the name of the call center won't do much if you still provide poor customer service delivered by unhappy agents. Before long you'll need to move away from your new brand for the same reasons that you abandoned your prior one.

Do Staff Respect and Support Your Organization?

Too often I've talked with employees in various industries who've disrespected their companies. They've said negative things about their bosses, their resources, and their compensation. After listening to their rants, I don't want to do business with those companies anymore and no amount of rebranding will ever fix that.

Instead of rebranding your call center, it's best to start with your agents. Are they proud of the work they do and the organization they work for? Are they paid an appropriate amount? If you say "yes" and they say "no," do some research to find out who's right. Adjust as needed.

Maybe you need to fix deficiencies in your management structure or operation processes. Perhaps you need to improve agent training, raise expectations, and hold staff accountable for the results. Alternately, you may need to hire a different caliber employee.

The point is to focus on staff, their environment, and the quality of their work before embarking on any rebranding efforts. If you don't, rebranding will fail to meet expectations, and in a few years, you'll be doing it all over again.

Conclusion

Though rebranding offers excitement and commands attention, don't pursue it until you've addressed the service behind your brand and the staff that provides it. Instead of looking to rebrand your call center, you might be better off tackling more critical items first.

Social Media and the Call Center

*Online Platforms Can Serve as Effective Communication
Channels for Customer Service, Promotions, and Marketing*

Attitudes about social media and online opportunities are varied. Some people dismiss them, some embrace them, and some merely tolerate them. Initially used as platforms for casual interpersonal interaction (that is, nonbusiness), organizations now tap the many variations of social media for enterprise communication.

For call centers, social media options and related internet opportunities fall into three categories.

1. Enhancing Operations

Social media offers the possibility to communicate with staff, recruit agents, and support a distributed workforce more effectively. Younger employees, who more typically embrace social media, especially appreciate these options.

2. Serving Your Organization

Just as every viable organization has a website, opportunities exist for them to also have a blog and social media presence. While certain departments, such as marketing, often take the lead in establishing and directing these efforts, call centers are in a unique position to provide ongoing frontline support on a day-to-day basis.

Even if marketing continually monitors and responds to social media posts, questions, and criticisms during normal business hours, who does this after regular hours—the time when consumers are more active on social platforms?

Your agents, who are already working evenings and weekends can react quickly, improving patient satisfaction and reducing frustration.

3. Connecting with Patients and Callers

The primary purpose of call centers is communicating with patients and callers. Consider some of these opportunities:

Email: This both precedes social media and provides an entry point to it. Apply everything you do with phone calls to email: answer emails, screen emails, route emails, add value to emails, prioritize emails, and escalate emails.

Chat: With chat, which is increasingly prevalent on websites, you can do the same things you currently do for telephone communications: answer questions, assist with site navigation, and (if your site sells products) keep visitors from abandoning their shopping cart.

Blog Comments: Though most blogs no longer allow comments, some still do. This allows readers to respond to posts. However, to protect against spam, these comments need review and approval beforehand or subsequent screening afterward.

This is something that a call center can easily do, especially since approval notifications can arrive via email. Additionally, a response to the comment is sometimes appropriate, allowing a dialogue to take place, be it within the blog's comment section or via another means.

Media Alerts: Automated services can scan cyberspace for occurrences of specific words or phrases, such as an organization's name or trademark. Although helpful, this information needs review and filtering before it becomes of practical use. A call center can receive these alerts, cull out the mismatches, and process the true matches as appropriate.

Implementation

Making a social media page is easy. Using it to its full potential is hard. First, to be of use, post relevant content on a regular basis.

Next, the people who like, follow, or engage with you on social media deserve interaction. When customer service issues, questions, or complaints surface, they warrant a quick response— before others chime in with their perspectives, which are often not helpful.

When responding, be sure to follow social media etiquette. Doing service or sales incorrectly on social media can produce unpleasant and even damaging results.

View social media as both a broadcast medium and a one-to-one communications channel. Replying to posts publicly and sending private messages are both great customer service opportunities, which align with the purpose of most call centers.

Conclusion

The internet offers many opportunities for meaningful connections to take place, with social media leading the way. The call center is in a unique position to manage these resources to make the most of these marketing and marketing-related communications.

Reputation, Referrals, and Credentials

Seek External Validation to Confirm Your Credibility

Your call center may be an in-house operation or an outsourcer that processes calls for other healthcare organizations. If you are an internal call center, you are either a profit center or a cost center. Outsource call centers are always profit centers.

You might also be under the control of another department, such as telecommunications, IT, or even marketing. In addition, there is the issue of who the call center director reports to. Does the director's superior understand the critical role that the call center plays in your organization? Do they comprehend your technological needs and the importance of a reliable infrastructure? Or is their primary concern that you don't make waves?

Regardless of the type of call center you work in, its place in the money stream, your department assignment, or your boss's affinity for your operation, there is a common need for increased, positive visibility. This is necessary in three areas.

The first is budgeting. The second is your center's ongoing viability and existence, that is, self-preservation. These both affect the funds you'll have access to for staffing, technology upgrades, and additional software. The third item is respect.

One option is to do nothing and hope for the best, which typically ends in frustration. The other option is to be proactive. Does this mean making demands and becoming a general irritant to upper management?

No. But it does mean taking careful and deliberate steps to elevate your call center to the point of earning the respect and admiration of the decision makers in your organization. This is a form of marketing.

There are three strategies to do this: reputation, referrals, and credentials.

Reputation

For your call center, reputation as a quality operation plays a critical role. Whether you are an outsourcing call center in search of new business or an in-house operation fighting for more funding or a better standing with upper management, your center's reputation will go a long way toward reaching your objective.

When a reputation for quality service, fair dealings, and ethical practices exists, your call center moves toward the top of the priority list. The opposite is true when negative connotations exist, frustrating marketing efforts and political efficacy. When you are a low priority, it requires more time and energy to make the sale, obtain your targeted funding, or garner your CEO's attention.

Although it takes time and focus to earn a positive reputation, the road to a bad one is much quicker. And once a negative reputation emerges, it's incredibly difficult to overcome. Reputation—either good or bad—is a great influencer of opinions, both internally and externally.

Referrals

For the outsource call center, the second and easiest way to gain new business is when others do the work for you. To obtain more business, you can ask clients if they know of others who could use your services. These leads are often prequalified and even presold.

Some outsource call centers have successfully added many new clients by merely asking existing clients for referrals. Some of these call centers elect to reward these *referring* clients with monetary or material gifts; others find that a sincere *thank you* garners even greater results.

The ultimate level of referral occurs when clients tell their associates about your call center and suggest they use your services. This is a sure sign of a delighted client. Sales via referrals occur when your actions match or even surpass your words—you don't just say what you will do, but you do what you say. You earn these referrals by providing quality service, reinforced by honorable business practices.

For the in-house call center, you do not need referrals to gain more business, but you do need all the friends you can find when it comes time to expand your department, get budget approval for new equipment or additional staff, or provide new services. If your center's work has earned the respect and admiration of others in your organization, they are much more likely to come to your aid when you need them.

Again, all you need to do is ask for help. When an agent receives a compliment, ask if they will pass it on to the manager, director, or upper management. Written compliments and recorded messages of accomplishment are even better, as you can easily share them with decision makers.

Credentials

Credentials are also important to call centers. You say and believe that your call center is the best, but can you prove it? Sure, you have callers or clients who say how much they value and appreciate the service you provide, and you have written testimonials about your quality and professionalism. But doesn't every call center have that? How can you truly distinguish yourself? To substantiate your call center's elevated level of excellence, you require credentials, and you need someone else to provide them.

A credential is verifiable recognition from an independent third party that you have achieved a standard level of performance. Having one credential puts your call center in a unique category that few can match. Having two or three moves you toward the top of any list.

There are three general types of credentials: agent testing, certification, and benchmarking. Each provides an independent, third-party validation of your call center's value.

Agent Testing: When I was in the operations side of the industry, I enrolled our call center in a third-party testing program. Initially, I viewed its results as a quality report card. It wasn't until after we earned their mark of affirmation that I realized it was also an important, powerful badge of distinction that we should promote.

In addition, the resulting scores provided hundreds of data points that could be analyzed to reveal areas of strength and weakness, as well as areas of consistency and inconsistency.

Consistency is important. As strange as it sounds, you may be better off being consistently weak in an area than inconsistent. At least when you're consistently weak, callers know what to expect and you deliver it every time.

Certification: Likewise, certification is when a third-party organization verifies that your call center meets and complies with certain preexisting and published criteria or values. The certification could range from technical expertise to agent quality or adhering to best-practice standards. (The inability to become certified could also signal a need for more funding, but advance this argument with care or it could backfire.)

Benchmarking: A third external source of credentials is benchmarking. Benchmarking focuses on quantitative call center measurements. For this reason, many CIOs and others in upper management like benchmarking. It gives a score on how one call center compares to other comparably sized operations.

A good benchmarking analysis will also indicate performance gaps (even the best call centers will have some), make recommendations on options to close those gaps (which is a great asset when working on the budget), and may even include a cost-benefit or return-on-investment analysis of those expenditures. Hence, benchmarking offers a quantitative score and is one more credential.

Whether you are pursuing a client, requesting more funding, or seeking better visibility in your organization, having some credentials to share will make your job a whole lot easier.

Use Email to Reach Out in the Right Way

Not All Communication Needs to Happen
over the Telephone

E mail is a cost-effective way to reach prospective patients. But just because it's cheap and easy doesn't mean it's always a wise idea. When done incorrectly, email messages can alienate the very audience you're trying to cultivate.

Send Only Useful Messages

I once had the grand idea of using an email-marketing program to keep advertisers (those folks who make *AnswerStat* possible) and potential advertisers informed and engaged. When I began working on each issue, I emailed them with the theme and deadlines. A week before the due date, I sent a reminder. When the magazine went to print, I dashed off an update. When it mailed, I let them know.

This lasted for one issue. Although sending the messages seemed free, it cost time. I also worried about annoying the recipients. (This was in the early days of email marketing, and I couldn't tell who was reading what I sent.)

I scaled back my messages to one per issue, and I stopped sending all but that first email, informing advertisers of the theme and deadlines. I hoped if I emailed less often, my recipients would be more willing to read what I did send.

Discover what messages matter most to your audience and then send only those.

Segment Your Audience

I quickly developed a rhythm of sending out one mass email per issue about advertising, but it wasn't as smooth as I had hoped. No matter how carefully I worded my email, I always confused someone. This resulted in follow-up communication to clear up my miscommunication.

I realized I was trying to make one message work for everyone: regular advertisers, occasional advertisers, and potential advertisers. But a message for regular advertisers might confuse the occasional ones. Alternately, a message encouraging potential advertisers to run an ad might irritate existing customers. To solve this, I divided my list into three groups, sending a different message tailored to each segment.

Your biggest stakeholder is different than your smallest, and both are different from your patients. Segment your list accordingly.

Send Only Wanted Messages

I email *AnswerStat* subscribers each time a new issue comes out. As part of their subscription, I also send occasional relevant messages that have a high likelihood of interest. So that I don't irritate readers, I send no more than one extra email per month. If you're like me, you've unsubscribed from organizations you liked simply because they emailed too often.

Determine how frequently you should email your audience. Know how often is too often and don't go beyond it.

Allow for Unsubscribes

Even though it's a legal requirement to provide a way to unsubscribe from your email list, I'm shocked at how many organizations don't follow this. In addition, some organizations let you click unsubscribe but don't follow through.

Make sure you allow for, and honor, unsubscribes.

Maintain List Integrity

Though I've never personally done it, email databases are easy to buy. It's also common for companies to harvest contact information from websites and directories. The result is sending messages to folks who didn't opt in. These messages are unethical and constitute spam.

In your zeal to communicate with as many individuals as possible, make sure you don't add people who didn't expressly opt in to your list.

Conclusion

Whether for customer service or marketing, when you send useful and wanted messages to your segmented list, allowing for unsubscribes and avoiding spam, you are on the right path to effective communication.

PART 6:

TECHNOLOGY
AND TOOLS

Arm Your Staff with the Tools They Need to Do the Job You
Ask Them to Do

Supplying your call center staff with the right technology empowers them to best accomplish the job you've asked them to do, to do the work they *want* to do, and to do their tasks with excellence.

Expecting them to function with distinction while saddled with hard-to-use, outdated, or complicated technology will frustrate them and hamper their ability to serve callers and patients to the best of their ability.

Skimp in this area to your call center's detriment. Or choose to make an investment that will pay off now and into the future.

Should You Use an On-Site System or Internet-Delivered Solution?

Make a Strategic Determination on the Best Platform
Option for Your Call Center

W e can understand a computer room full of equipment. It's tangible. We can see it, touch it, and even kick it (not recommended). It's how we've done things for decades since the beginning of computers and telephony switches.

Contrast this to internet-delivered solutions, which, in general, go by a myriad of names, such as SaaS (software as a service), cloud-based solutions, hosted services, and a few more labels that have come and gone. The oldest name I remember is ASP (application service provider). For the sake of discussion, let's call all variations of this offsite provisioning concept as internet-delivered solutions.

Here are the pros and cons of each option.

On Premise

An on-site system allows for greater control. But with control comes responsibility: maintenance, database backups, software updates, spare parts inventory, disaster recovery, backup power, and technical staff. Financially, an on-site system (hardware and software) represents a tangible asset, which is a capitalized purchase and a depreciated line item on your balance sheet.

While there are usually some ongoing costs for an on-site system, these are minor in comparison to the one-time purchase price. An on-site system doesn't require internet access to operate, but with the increased need to access information and remote systems through the internet, this advantage is rapidly diminishing.

Although vendor stability is a concern for both options, with on-site systems, there is at least the potential for the call center to continue operating if the vendor fails, which is not the case with the alternative.

Internet-Delivered Solutions

Internet-delivered solutions represent a newer way of provisioning a call center. With the responsibility to install, maintain, and update equipment removed from the equation, along with it goes the associated control.

Financially, an internet-delivered solution is a service, which shows up on the income statement as an expense. It is not a capital expenditure, and there is nothing to depreciate. The only cost is a predictable, ongoing monthly expense, which is proportional to usage.

Internet-delivered solutions also offer the flexibility to quickly ramp up and ramp down capacity as needed. You may deploy operations anywhere in the world where there is reliable internet access, easily accommodating remote agents.

However, there are two chief concerns with cloud-based solutions.

One is the requirement of a stable internet connection for the call center and remote agents. Without internet access, the call center is effectively down.

The other concern is with the vendor. Do they provide always-on, fully redundant, carrier-grade stability, with 24/7 tech support? Are they financially viable to offer cloud-based service for the long-term? If they stumble or fail, your call center immediately suffers the same fate.

Select the Option That's Right for You

For much of the call center industry's history, on-site systems were the only option. Some call centers continue to pursue this approach, not because they've examined the alternative, but because that's how it's always been. They see no point in changing. This is shortsighted.

Equally unwise are call centers that race headlong into internet-delivered solutions, wanting merely to follow the current trend. They dismiss the alternative without consideration, simply because it's the old way of doing things. An unexamined strategy, however, is really no strategy at all.

Neither approach is universally right. Both have advantages; both have disadvantages. Take a careful look at the pros and cons of each option. Then make a strategic decision on which one is the best for you and your call center. Your organization's future may be at stake.

IVR's Place in the Call Center

Turn Interactive Voice Response from a
Liability into an Asset

IVR (Interactive Voice Response) has its place in the call center, but we need not overstate what that place is. If IVR can truly speed up the call for the caller or gather information to assist the agent in providing better service, then use it. However, when the primary goal of IVR becomes to save money, reduce the agent headcount, or limit customer service options, rethink your strategy and desired outcomes.

IVR Dos:

- Always provide an option for the caller to press zero to talk to an agent.
- Provide short and basic options that someone from outside your organization can readily understand.
- Ask your patients, and even your friends, to call and test your IVR. Then fix the things that bug them.
- Set up your call center's IVR exactly as you would want one to work when you call someone else.

IVR Don'ts:

- Don't block the digit zero. The customer is always right, and if the customer wants to talk to a person, let them.
- Don't prompt for an account number if the agent is going to ask for it again.
- Don't have callers make entries (such as for "billing") and then not tell the agent which option they selected.
- Don't route callers to a general agent queue after they've taken the time to tell the IVR why they're calling. Skip the subterfuge, and just route the call.
- Don't provide level after level of menu options. Keep it simple.
- Don't force a mildly irritated patient through a frustratingly long or cumbersome IVR tree. If you do, they'll exit it highly irritated and take it out on the agent.

Summary

IVR has its place, but IVR in most call centers suffers from a poor configuration and needs an implementation overhaul.

What are you doing about it in your call center?

~

Call Recording in Your Call Center

*Use Recordings for Training, Quality Assurance,
and Much More*

Once thought of as a call center luxury, the original function of call recorders was to resolve he-said/she-said dilemmas. All too often, the caller claimed one thing, but the agent had an opposite perspective. Management then faced a quandary of whom to believe. Without a means to verify the details, all the call center manager could do was apologize. But call recorders solved this problem.

Uses of Call Recording

Call recordings, however, are no longer just a way to prove who said what. Call recorders have proven themselves invaluable as a training tool, for agent self-evaluation, and in quality control, as well as for dispute resolution and call verification.

Training: Agent training can use call recordings. One application is to capture examples of exemplary calls by seasoned agents for trainees to review and emulate.

Conversely, trainers can use less-than-ideal calls for discussion and critique. Although both scenarios can use fictitious examples or staged calls, there's great benefit in being able to demonstrate real-world examples.

Self-evaluation: A powerful tool of introspection occurs when agents use call recorders to retrieve their own calls and go through a process of self-discovery to learn how they can handle calls or situations more effectively.

Although this is valuable during the training phase, it's also beneficial for experienced agents, as it allows them to keep their skills sharp and helps sloppy actions from becoming unhealthy habits.

Even more importantly, agents may specifically seek out and review a specific call that had a less-than-ideal result so they can achieve a more desirable outcome on future calls.

Quality Assurance: With call recording, supervisors and managers can easily and quickly retrieve, review, and evaluate agent calls for their quality assurance (QA) program.

By integrating a program of silent monitoring, with side-by-side coaching and statistical measurements, supervisors can evaluate and verify an agent's overall effectiveness. Call recording allows for the discovery of areas needing correction and items to celebrate.

Dispute Resolution: Whether it is a message, a medical emergency, or an accusation of improper phone behavior, the voice recording of a disputed call becomes an independent third-party account of what happened. This avoids he-said/she-said disputes in which neither party can prove their account of what happened.

Though the agent is sometimes in error, in most cases the recording exonerates the agent. When the aggrieved party hears the recording, the problem usually resolves itself without further effort.

Verification: Another worthwhile use of call recording occurs when communicating critical health information, such as in telephone triage. Call recordings capture the symptoms and the nurse's instructions to the patient to verify that they conveyed proper information. Normally, the recording is never listened to unless there is a concern with the transaction.

Legal Considerations

Before you record any phone calls, check with an attorney familiar with state and national laws for clarification about legal requirements and concerns.

The biggest issue is whether one or both parties need to know that recording is taking place. Always notify agents when call recording is happening. Notification to the patient or caller can occur in a preamble recording (for example: "This call may be monitored or recorded for quality assurance purposes").

I am not a lawyer, and this is not legal advice, but a best practice may be to notify both parties regardless of the legal requirements for your location. This seems like the proper and ethical thing to do.

Summary

Call recording has emerged as a critical tool for call center managers and their frontline staff. When properly implemented and fully used, call recordings can help with training, agent self-evaluation, quality control, dispute resolution, and call verification.

Voice AI in the Healthcare Call Center

Should We Embrace Technology or Fear It?

Throughout the history of the call center industry, we've sought ways to help agents be more effective. In the pre-computer days this meant physical solutions and electro-mechanical devices that allowed staff to answer calls faster, record information easier, and organize data more effectively.

Then came rudimentary computers that provided basic call distribution and CTI (computer telephony integration). Computer databases allowed us to retrieve information and store data. Following this we experienced voicemail, IVR (interactive voice response), and automated attendant. More recently we've encountered speech-to-text conversion and text-to-speech applications. Then came the chatbots, computerized automatons that allow for basic text and voice communication between machines and people.

Computers are talking with us. Phones too. Technology marches forward. What will happen next?

I did an online search for voice AI. Within .5 seconds I received two billion results. The first few matches gave me some eye-opening and thought-provoking content to read and watch. In considering this online information, however, it's hard to determine what's practical application for the near future and what's theoretical potential that might never happen.

However, with advances in chatbot technology, artificial intelligence (AI), and machine learning, we aren't far from the time when computer applications will carry on full, convincing conversations with callers who will think they're talking with real people.

While many pieces of this puzzle are available today, we're not yet to the point where we can have a complete, intelligent dialogue with a computer and not know it. But it will happen. Probably soon.

Regardless, the voice AI software will need the backup support of real people to address what it can't do or correct what it did wrong.

So, let's embrace these technology advances as inevitable and not fear them.

What Does AI Mean for the Medical Call Center?

*Embrace Tools to Serve Patients More Effectively and Help
Staff Do Their Jobs Better*

All technological advances since the inception of call centers continue to free agents from basic tasks and allow them to handle more complex issues. Technology will not replace agents, but it will shift their primary responsibilities.

Or maybe not.

With the application of voice AI, might we one day have a call center staffed solely with computer algorithms instead of telephone agents? I don't know. Anything I say today will seem laughable in the future. Either I will have overstretched technology's potential or underestimated the speed of its advance. I've done both.

I think I'm okay talking to a computer program to make an appointment with my doctor. And it wouldn't bother me to call in the evening and converse with a computer as I leave my message for the doctor, nurse, or office staff. However, what concerns me just a tad would be calling a telephone triage number and having a computer give me medical advice.

Yet, in considering the pieces of technology available to us today, this isn't so far-fetched. Defined and proven triage protocols exist, stored in a database. Giving them a computerized voice is possible. And with AI and machine learning, the potential exists for an intelligent interface to provide the conversational bridge between me and the protocols. This could be the solution to the growing shortage of medical practitioners.

Those of you doing telephone triage may be laughing right now. Or perhaps you're already implementing this. Maybe you're convinced it will never work at all.

Yet it's important that we talk about technology and its application in healthcare call centers. Regardless of what happens, the future will certainly be an interesting place.

The Internet of Things Intersects Healthcare

Consider a Future Where Your Call Center Interacts with Both Patients and Things

The term *Internet of Things* (IoT) may be new to you, or it might be something you've already grown weary of. Though a definition for the IoT is still evolving, expect to hear a lot more about it in the future.

The Internet of Things revolves around the concept of things—instead of people—using the internet to share information without the need for human interaction. Though a "thing" implies a device, it could refer to any object and include animals or even people. At the most basic level, an active RFID (radio frequency identification) tag qualifies as part of the IoT.

Common or Near-Future Applications

A huge area of interest for the IoT is in home automation and convenience. A security system is one obvious application, where sensors in your home report to a computer at the monitoring station about what's happening when you're away. Internet-connected garage doors are a reality today, as well as remotely accessible thermostats, babysitter cams, and door locks.

Looking into the future, the IoT could report when your kids get home from school, who's come with them, and if they leave again, as well as their school attendance record. Dreaming a bit more, your kitchen might make a grocery list for you based on the contents of your cupboards and refrigerator and even place the order for you.

Fitness

Another area for the IoT is fitness.

Devices—whether a stand-alone gadget or a phone app—can track how many steps we take in a day. With an internet connection, this data uploads to another computer for analysis, storage, or action, such as texting the patient to encourage them to take an evening walk because they haven't gotten their steps in.

Fitness devices can also monitor basic body functions such as heart rate, moving the IoT more fully into healthcare.

Healthcare

Healthcare is rife with applications, both present and future, for the IoT. Monitoring patients' vital signs is common in the hospital environment, but now the concept can extend to home-based convalescence or hospice. Telehealth taps into the IoT and can expand because of it.

Locating dementia patients who may have wandered off is feasible with the IoT. Even remotely administering medications is a possibility. The only limit to realizing these grand healthcare applications is our ability to imagine them.

While the basic premise is that the IoT moves data without human interaction, at a certain point some of this data will require human involvement. This may be to evaluate options, initiate a response, or escalate action when reaching a preset threshold. The IoT becomes a serious tool to keep us healthy and safe. Lives are at stake.

The Contact Center

At the intersection of healthcare and the IoT stands the modern healthcare contact center. The medically minded call center already has the staffing and technological infrastructure in place to handle such tasks. Some call centers are already doing some of these things to serve patients and assist healthcare providers, though they may not have considered them in the context of tapping into the IoT.

Opportunities abound. To be ready to make the most of them, look at the healthcare-related IoT around you. Then investigate what your contact center needs to handle the required human aspect on the back end. It may be a bit of specific training or some server software that provides the needed interface.

Be ready so that when someone comes to you with a problem stemming from the flood of data from the IoT, you can nod and smile when you tell them, "Yes, we are IoT-enabled and ready to help."

PART 7:

SEASONAL CONSIDERATIONS

Let the Annual Calendar Guide You in Making a Difference Now and in the Next Year

W e'll wrap up our discussion with some considerations tied to annual holidays: Thanksgiving, Christmas, and New Year's Day. Each one provides both an opportunity for personal and staff-wide celebration, as well as the occasion to positively impact your staff, your community, and the future of your call center. Even if you don't personally embrace these holidays, use their appearance on the calendar to enhance your healthcare call center operation.

I wish you the best as you do.

Remember to Be Thankful

*In the Middle of Struggles, Turmoil, and Difficulties, Pause
to Celebrate the Positive*

The United States, along with a few other countries, celebrates Thanksgiving in November. Canada and some other nations do so in October.

Regardless of when you celebrate Thanksgiving—or even if it's not a holiday where you live—take a moment to remember and give thanks for the positive elements in your life. Encourage your staff to do the same.

With all that is happening in our world, it's easy to focus on the negative, which can pull us down with discouragement and overwhelm us with despair. Yet there are positive things happening as well. We need to acknowledge and embrace them.

Here are some things to be thankful for.

Be Thankful for Health

I take my health for granted—until I get sick. Then I'm reminded to appreciate the rest of the time when I'm healthy, which is most every day.

Even though few people have zero health concerns, with health status existing on a continuum, let's be thankful for the positive aspects and not wallow in the negative.

Be Thankful for Work

No job is 100 percent perfect, but having a job in the first place—when others don't—is a huge reason to be thankful. Our jobs allow us to earn a living to support ourselves and our families.

Without it, we'd have to rely on the generosity of others or the support of government. Next time your work hasn't gone so well—and it will happen—wrap up the day by giving thanks that you have a job. Not everyone does.

Be Thankful for Friends

True friendships don't occur easily for most people. We have acquaintances, coworkers, and neighbors, but that doesn't necessarily make them friends. We should celebrate the friendships we do have, the friendships that enhance our life.

And if you're a bit short in the friend department, remember that to find a friend, you need to first be a friend.

Be Thankful for Family

Though we can choose our friends, we can't choose our family. They're ours for life; never take them for granted.

May we celebrate each family relationship for the good parts and overlook the rest.

Be Thankful for Opportunity

If you find it difficult to be thankful in one of the above areas—health, work, family, or friends—because you don't see it as part of your life or are experiencing a shortfall, don't fret. The future provides an opportunity to change the present.

Starting today, you can work to improve your health, make your job more meaningful, grow your friendships, and embrace your family. But to make the most of this opportunity, you must first seize it.

And that opportunity is another thing to be thankful for.

The Season for Giving

Helping Others Benefits Them—and Us

After Thanksgiving comes Christmas, a festive time that inspires a spirit of giving. Embrace this attitude in your call center. We need this because working in a call center is challenging and demanding. Daily activity all too often consists only of reacting to the urgency of the moment. There is little time to plan and few opportunities to look beyond the confines of the call center.

Yet, looking beyond is exactly what's needed. Seeking ways to give back to your community may be precisely what you need to do. Some call centers have done so with profound results.

Why Give

There are many reasons for a call center to give back to its community. Aside from principled reasons, the practical justification is that it is good for business. Community involvement expands networking opportunities, increases corporate standing, and generates goodwill.

From an employee standpoint, it builds team camaraderie as staffers serve together and pursue common non-work-related goals. Community involvement also increases employer esteem and provides a connection outside the workplace. These, then, have the indirect effect of improving employee job satisfaction and decreasing turnover. Lastly, as employees see a new and different side to their employer, respect will increase, nurturing a better mutual understanding. With all these benefits, what call center wouldn't want to promote and pursue a philanthropic effort?

What to Give

There are primarily two forms of assistance: money and time. Many organizations are more in need of volunteer labor than they are of monetary donations.

Let's start with labor. You can provide opportunities for your staff to volunteer. They can go in groups. It's easier to go somewhere new or try something different when you take a friend with you. In addition, there is the bonus of being able to serve together. This has its own rewards.

Most of these opportunities occur outside regular working hours. Some businesses have a provision to take time off without pay. A few even offer paid time off to volunteer. These, however, are rare, costly to the company, and often not needed. Setting up a straightforward way to let staff know about and pursue volunteer opportunities takes little time and incurs minimal cost.

For many people, it's much easier to write a check than it is to volunteer. The same is true for businesses. But if a corporate financial donation is not feasible, don't worry about it. Having you and your staff involved is more important anyway.

If making a financial contribution is feasible, one consideration is setting up a matching fund. This is when companies budget monies to match the donations of their employees. The employee makes the donation, submits the receipt, and the company makes a matching contribution. This, too, is quite easy to set up. Payroll deductions for charities are also an option, but they are more costly and time-consuming to implement. Of course, there is also the option for the call center to make a direct contribution.

Where to Give

Needs exist all around your community. Find out what is already going on. Consider after-school programs, food pantries, clothes closets, homeless shelters, and soup kitchens. Call your nearest school and ask how you can help. Opportunities might include "adopt-a-classroom," reading programs, tutoring, providing back-to-school supplies, or helping with GED classes.

If you have a college nearby, check with the service organizations on campus and see how you can support them. A side benefit of working with college students is that you will be interacting with potential job candidates. Just make sure that agent prospecting doesn't become the only reason for getting involved.

Who to Give To

By now, I suspect your mind is spinning with ideas. There are so many needs, so many opportunities, and there is so much to do. However, these needs can quickly overwhelm, which leads to discouragement, which results in inaction. The key to prevent this from occurring is to whittle down the list. Identify *one* organization that is a good fit and focus on how you can help them.

Start by asking your employees to make recommendations. They will tend to suggest groups they already support with their time or money. Although only a small percentage of your staff will currently be involved with any organization, start there. They already have a connection and an affiliation. As a bonus, they can acclimate others as they step forward to volunteer.

You will also have some staffers who want to help a particular organization but have not taken that first step. Their recommendations are also worth considering. Again, their desire to help that organization provides an easier connection.

Before you make a final selection, perform "due diligence," just as you would for an important business purchase or partnership. For nonprofits, find out how long they've been in your community and check out their annual reports. Ask what percentage of donations goes to overhead. See if the Better Business Bureau has a file on them or what the Chamber of Commerce may know. If things look good, meet with the executive director, ask to attend a board meeting, and seek a straightforward way to test if you are a good fit for each other.

Regardless of the size of your call center, pick just one organization to support—at least initially. It's far better to make a significant and sustained effort with one group than to target many organizations ineffectively. Only after you have successfully shown ongoing support for one organization should you consider a second one—if you want to. But proceed with care.

Remember that, for many call centers, focusing on one group is the ideal.

How to Give

Once you have selected a group to work with and identified an initial area of service, it's time for action. Ideally, call center leadership should be in this first wave of volunteering, setting the example and inspiring others to follow. As mentioned, it's easier to go as a group, especially for the first few times.

If one or more of your employees have already volunteered with the organization, let them take the lead, easing others in and showing them how to do things. In no time, everyone will be serving with practiced confidence. Now this group can repeat the process with others.

It's important to remember that no matter how great the need or how rewarding the work, only a percentage of employees will take part and their degree of involvement will vary greatly. Expect this to occur. Just make sure no one feels obligated to get involved. Remind them that volunteering is, in fact, voluntary. You don't want to serve with someone who is negative or resentful. The goal is to have fun and find fulfillment as you volunteer. Leave the naysayers at home.

When to Give

Now. Not next month, not next year. Now. And not just at the holidays but year-round too.

Finish Strong and Don't Just Slide into the New Year

How You Conclude This Year Will Prepare You for What Happens Next Year

As you anticipate a new year for the healthcare call center, you may turn the calendar with expectations for a better future. At the same time, you may wonder how much change you'll see. Regardless of the situation, the future looms as a huge question. But know that what you do today—and in the remaining days of this year—will influence what you experience next year.

Here are some things to consider.

Make Flexible Plans

As you look forward to the new year, develop a strategy with contingencies. Do it now. Factor in options. This means developing a plan A *and* a plan B *and* even a plan C. It means considering tactics for how to do things in person *and* remotely. Look to implement technology that can adapt to accommodate expectations as needed, regardless of what path the future takes. Assume that what you're doing today in your call center will change as you move throughout next year.

Don't Coast

The understandable temptation, especially as a grueling year winds down, is to relax. You're worn out and want a break. You've worked hard and deserve to take it easy. Though resting has its merits, this isn't justification to check out and coast through this year's remaining days.

Resist the temptation to make up for taking a break now by promising to hit the ground running on January 2. By then inertia will have set in, and it will take too long to get back up to speed. Breezing through work for a few weeks may seem like an attractive option, but the big-picture perspective is that you run the risk of not being ready to embrace a new year.

Be Intentional

Be deliberate in how you wind down the final days of December. This doesn't mean accelerating at full speed, but don't hit the brakes either. Look to wrap up projects so that you don't have to carry them into a new year. Pursue small initiatives now to form a foundation you can build on to produce success faster when you return to work after the holidays.

May you finish strong this year and move with confident preparedness into the next.

Prepare Now to Make Next Year Great

Failing to Plan Is Planning to Fail

B efore the year ends, take time to envision what you want next year to be like. Plan and prepare now to make it a wonderful one. Though it's possible you've already done this, maybe you hope to do so in the next couple of weeks.

However, I wonder if in the day-to-day crunch of call center work that you're so focused on getting through today that you never have time to think about what's next. This is the tyranny of the urgent. It's the reality that putting out fires consumes all your day, leaving no time to pursue what's most important. This includes planning for future success.

Don't let the tyranny of the urgent limit what your call center, department, shift, or team accomplishes in the coming year. To inspire your thoughts and get you started, here are some ideas to help make next year the best year yet:

Celebrate Areas of Excellence

Every call center has things it does well. Don't lose sight of this. Take a mental inventory of what you and your operation excel at. Revel in all your successes.

Then take steps to ensure these skills don't slip away. Also consider ways to make them even better.

Identify Areas That Need Fixing

Conversely, even the best call centers can do better. Everyone has flaws in their operation, processes, or human resources. Start by identifying these so you can prepare to fix them next year.

Look for Growth Potential

Though no one can predict the future with any certainty, you can look at trends and consider areas where you can grow your call center to offer new services or expand existing ones. This gives us a chance to dream. And—lest you consider this exercise self-serving—remember that everyone likes to be part of a growing operation. Make sure your call center is expanding and not shrinking.

Consider Pressures to Your Call Center

While there's the potential for growth, there's also the potential for contraction. This isn't as exciting to think about, but it's important to give it attention. What issues does your call center face that could have a detrimental effect on it in the coming year? Theorize the top three pressures that could have a negative impact on your call center. Then plan to counteract them, offset them, or negate their power.

Conclusion

The above four items are strengths, weaknesses, opportunities, and threats (also known as SWOT). Yes, I just encouraged you to conduct a SWOT analysis for your healthcare call center. But don't look at this with foreboding; embrace it with excitement.

Then use your SWOT analysis to plan for the coming year: capitalize on your strengths, shore up your weaknesses, pursue opportunities, and guard against threats. Turn this into an action plan. Establish a vision and set goals. If you do this, you'll have a much better year.

May next year be your best year ever.

The Future of the Healthcare Call Center Industry

The prospect of healthcare call centers shines bright.

Expect the function of call centers to continue to expand in the provisioning of healthcare services and the support of those efforts. We can anticipate that anything that doesn't require in-person interaction will migrate online. Though this can be in the form of a telephone call, other communication channels will grow in their use, functionality, and popularity.

In this regard, expect video calls to emerge as the next frontier of patient interaction. Also, know that some of these channel options may not even exist yet.

The last few years have proven—to the industry specifically, and society overall—that healthcare call centers can play a critical part in helping to meet the growing healthcare needs of patients. Healthcare call centers stand at a crossroads, poised to take on an even more prominent role in the future.

Accelerating this trend is a lack of qualified workers in every industry, which is even more pronounced in healthcare. The current shortage of healthcare practitioners will only intensify as we move into the future. This directly applies to telephone triage operations who stand poised to meet this burgeoning need. Yet each healthcare call center can rise to meet the staffing shortage that faces every organization, expanding the scope, stature, and significance of their operation as they do.

This opportunity, however, points to the critical need for healthcare call centers themselves to take the steps required so they can ensure they have trained personnel who are ready to meet this increasing need. This looms as the biggest hurdle for healthcare call centers to clear.

This need to address and even overhaul human resource paradigms and practices reminds us of the requirement to expect— and even embrace—change as you move forward. Those operations that welcome change and can incorporate new opportunities and mindsets into their organization will see a very bright future, one budding with much potential.

In the future, expect technology to play an increasingly important function in all that you do in your call center, your *contact* center. But here's what will never change. The primary objective of healthcare call centers is to provide people to help people.

Keep this in mind and you will thrive.

Acknowledgments

I sincerely thank the following companies that have helped cover the production costs of this book. Without them, this book wouldn't be possible.

1Call

The 1Call Division of Amtelco (1call.com) congratulates Peter on another successful publication about the unique requirements of call centers in the healthcare environment. As a partner of an ever-expanding number of healthcare call centers around the world, 1Call streamlines enterprise-wide communications and simplifies interoperability by providing a single source of truth. 1Call's seamless integrations combined with ease-of-use help care teams respond faster, resulting in better patient care. 1Call offers a comprehensive collection of modular applications designed to deliver fast access to current on-call schedules, directories, secure messaging, notification services, and scripted workflows for an entire enterprise.

LVM Systems

LVM has developed healthcare contact center solutions for over three decades to support both clinical and marketing functions. As a dedicated partner, LVM brings to the table employees averaging 15.5 years in the industry.

Today's hospitals need integrated solutions that improve access through interoperability. Integrating omni-communication tools such as chat, group texting, secure messaging, and email, in addition to the phone, enables healthcare organizations to serve their consumers' needs more effectively.

LVM understands leveraging technologies like phone interfaces, speech-to-text, real-time dashboards, ad-hoc reporting, web-based products, and sharing data with EMRs are critical to gaining efficiencies. Contact LVM Systems (lvmsystems.com) at 480-633-8200, ext. 286.

MedCall Plus

MedCall Plus is the healthcare industry's leading provider of telephone answering service and call center support services to the healthcare community. MedCall Plus offers insourced and outsourced solutions for each department of your busy medical practice or healthcare organization. MedCall Plus brings forty years of medically focused communication management expertise to help you affordably transform the patient experience.

MedCall Plus offers medical answering service to power your patient contact experience and can provide appointment scheduling, patient access solutions, medical answering service, insource and outsourcing solutions, EMR integration, and contact center consultation. Learn more at callcenter-salespro.com/medcallplus.

About Peter Lyle DeHaan

Peter Lyle DeHaan, PhD, is the publisher and editor-in-chief of *AnswerStat* magazine and *Medical Call Center News,* covering the healthcare call center industry. Peter's lifetime of experience includes managing a multi-location call center, employment with a call center vendor, and consultant for healthcare call centers, medical answering services, and telephone answering providers. You can find out more at PeterLyleDeHaan.com.

Other Books by Peter Lyle DeHaan

For a complete, up-to-date list of Peter's books, go to PeterLyle-DeHaan.com.

Sticky Customer Service: Stop Churning Customers and Start Growing Your Business

How to Start a Telephone Answering Service

with more on the way!

Made in United States
Orlando, FL
24 June 2023

34488431R00108